It's another Quality Book from CGP

This book is for anyone doing AQA Coordinated Science at GCSE.

It contains lots of tricky questions designed
to make you sweat — because that's the only
way you'll get any better.

It's also got some daft bits in to try and make
the whole experience at least vaguely
entertaining for you.

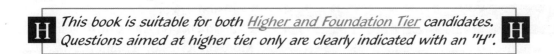

H This book is suitable for both _Higher and Foundation Tier_ candidates. H
Questions aimed at higher tier only are clearly indicated with an "H".

What CGP is all about

Our sole aim here at CGP is to produce the highest quality
books — carefully written, immaculately presented and
dangerously close to being funny.

Then we work our socks off to get them out to you
— at the cheapest possible prices.

Contents

Published by Coordination Group Publications Ltd.

Contributors: Paddy Gannon, Chris Dennett, Tim Major, Becky May, Katherine Reed.

ISBN 1-84146-969-6
Groovy website: www.cgpbooks.co.uk
Printed by Elanders Hindson, Newcastle upon Tyne.
Text, design, layout and original illustrations © Richard Parsons.

The Three States of Matter

Answer these questions.

Q1 Name the **three states** of matter.

Q2 Name the **theory** that explains the major differences between these states of matter.

Q3 In each of the boxes below, **draw a diagram** to show the arrangements of the particles in these three states of matter (they have been started for you).

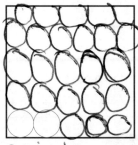
Name: Solids

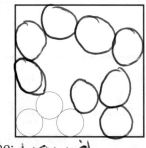
Name: Liquid

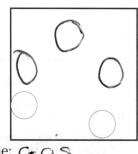
Name: Gas

Q4 Sort the following phrases into lists that describe the properties of each state of matter.

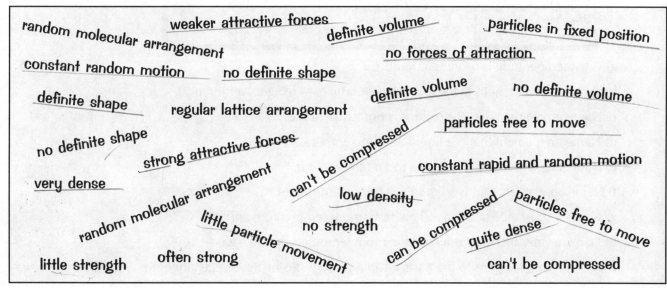

weaker attractive forces
random molecular arrangement
definite volume
particles in fixed position
constant random motion
no forces of attraction
no definite shape
definite shape
regular lattice arrangement
definite volume
no definite volume
no definite shape
strong attractive forces
particles free to move
very dense
can't be compressed
constant rapid and random motion
random molecular arrangement
little particle movement
low density
no strength
can be compressed
quite dense
particles free to move
little strength
often strong
can't be compressed

Q5 **a)** Which state of matter is the **strongest**? Why?

b) Which state will have the least particles in a given volume? **Explain** why.

c) For a given substance, which state of it will have the most energy? **Explain** why.

d) Which **state** will water be in at: -10°C, 10°C, 110°C (under normal atmospheric pressure)? What is the **common name** for each state?

e) Why is it **difficult** to squash liquids? **Give an example** of something that might use this property.

f) Gases can be squashed. What does this tell you about the distance between gas particles?

g) **Explain** how a gas exerts pressure on the sides of its container.

h) What would happen to the **pressure** of a gas if you increased its temperature in a rigid container? **Why** would this happen?

Top Tips: You need to know **all** the differences between solids, liquids and gases and **how** their properties make them suitable for various jobs. These **physical properties** can all be explained by **how close** the particles are and **how fast** they're moving — easy, eh.

The Three States of Matter

Answer these questions:

Q6 Give four **everyday examples** of each of the three states of matter.

Q7 **Complete** the following diagram by naming each change of state — A, B, C, and D.

A	B
Solid	Liquid	Gas
D	C

Q8 **a)** Where does the energy supplied to the solid or liquid always go?

b) What does this make happen?

c) What has to be overcome for a solid to change to a liquid, and a liquid to a gas?

Q9 Use the table below to answer the questions that follow it:

Substance	Melting Point (°C)	Boiling Point (°C)
Zinc	420	907
Oxygen	-238	-183
Bromine	-7	59
Mercury	-39	357

a) What temperature is **room temperature?** *25*

b) Which element melts at the **lower temperature** — oxygen or mercury? *oxygen*

c) Name an element that is a **solid** at room temperature.

d) Name an element that is a **liquid** at room temperature. *water*

e) Name an element that is a **gas** at room temperature. *oxygen*

f) Name an element that is a **liquid** at a temperature of **60°C.** *hot water*

g) Name a substance that is a **solid** at both room temperature and **200°C.** *stone*

h) Name a substance that is a **liquid** at room temperature, but a **gas** at **100°C.**

i) **Explain** what happens to the particles in a **solid** as it is heated and changes to a **liquid.**

j) **Explain** in your own words what **evaporation** is.

Q10 Look at the graph opposite.

This shows how the temperature of wax changes as it is cooled. **Explain** why the graph has two flat sections.

(**Words to use:** *Condensing, freezing, temperature, particles, flat sections*).

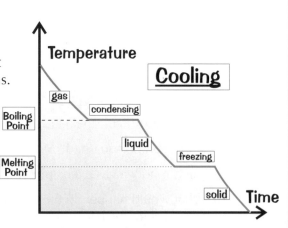

Temperature

Cooling

gas
Boiling Point — condensing
liquid
freezing
Melting Point —
solid → Time

Q11 **Describe** what happens to the particles in water when it freezes.

Top Tips: Changes of **state** mean **heat energy** is going **in** or **out** of the substance — the **more energy** in a substance, the **faster** the particles can move . With this fact you'll explain what's **happening** in changes of state and **interpret** cooling and heating curves with ease.

Atoms and Molecules

From the diagrams, choose the letter of the pictures that best describe:

Q1 A **pure** element.

Q2 A **pure** compound.

Q3 A **mixture** of elements.

Q4 A **mixture** of compounds.

Q5 An example of molecules made from just **two elements**.

Q6 An example of molecules made from **three elements**.

Q7 Which example could be **water**?

Q8 Which example could be **carbon monoxide**?

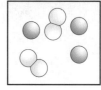

A   B   C

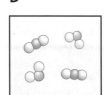
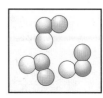

D   E   F

Q9 Methane can be represented in the following ways:

Molecular formula CH_4

Structural formula
$$H-\overset{\displaystyle H}{\underset{\displaystyle H}{C}}-H$$

Molecular model

Complete the table for the following named substances:

Name	Molecular formula	Structural formula	Molecular model
Water		$H\overset{O}{}H$	
Ammonia	NH_3		
Ethane		$H-\overset{H}{\underset{H}{C}}-\overset{H}{\underset{H}{C}}-H$	
Carbon dioxide			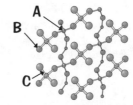

The diagram shows a molecular model of silicon dioxide.

Q10 Use the following words to label A, B and C:

Silicon   oxygen   covalent bond

A
B
C

Top Tips: **Atoms** join up to make **molecules**. The "join" is a **chemical bond** and the arrangement of atoms is shown in a molecular model. You can show a molecule as a **molecular formula** or a **structural formula,** or build a **three dimensional model** with little balls and sticks, which is more fun.

Atoms

Q1   Answer these questions on atoms:

a) What is an **atom**?

b) **How many** different subatomic particles make up an atom?

c) What are their **names**?

d) What is a **nucleus**?

e) What is an **electron shell**?

Q2   **Complete the labels** A, B and C on the diagram opposite.

Q3   **Complete** the table below:

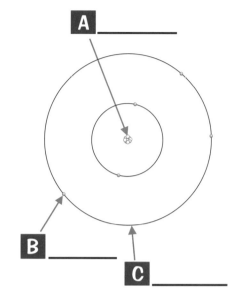

Particle	Mass	Charge	Where it is found
Proton	1		
Electron		-1	
Neutron			In the nucleus

Q4   More details on atoms:

a) **Where** is most of the mass in an atom concentrated?

b) What is in between the **nucleus** and the **electrons**?

Q5   An atom is about 10^{-10}m in diameter. **How many** would fit in a line across a pin head 0.1mm wide?

Q6   What part of the atom do nuclear reactions affect?

Q7   All atoms are neutral. If an atom has seven electrons then **how many** protons does it have?

Q8   Answer these questions on the atomic number and mass number of an element:

a) What does the **atomic number** tell us?

b) What does the **mass number** tell us?

c) What do the letters A and Z in the diagram stand for? What is A - Z?

d) **How many** protons are there in an atom of lithium?

e) **How many** electrons are there in an atom of lithium?

f) **How many** neutrons are there in an atom of lithium?

g) Which **number** _(mass or atomic)_ determines what element an atom is?

$$A \searrow \, ^{7}\text{Li}$$
$$Z \nearrow \, ^{3}$$

Q9   **Calculate** the number of protons, electrons and neutrons in the following:

a) Carbon ($^{12}_{6}\text{C}$)   b) Potassium ($^{39}_{19}\text{K}$)   c) Hydrogen ($^{1}_{1}\text{H}$).

Q10   Some questions on isotopes:

a) What are **isotopes**?

b) **Give an example** of an isotope used in dating old objects.

c) Uranium 235 and Uranium 238 are isotopes. Are they chemically different? **Explain** why.

Q11   **Calculate** the number of protons, electrons and neutrons in:

a) Deuterium ($^{2}_{1}\text{H}$)   b) Tritium ($^{3}_{1}\text{H}$)

Top Tips: Some tricky new terms here — that's science for you. You must know the difference between **atomic** number and **mass** number. Doing questions like this is excellent practice — come the Exam, it'll be easy marks. Bet you can't wait...

Electron Arrangement

Answer these atom questions:

Q1   An atom can be compared to the solar system. **Explain** the similarity.

Q2   What keeps the electrons **attracted** to the nucleus?

Q3   Give **another** name for an electron orbit.

Q4   **Complete** the table to show the sizes of the electron shells:

Electron shell	Maximum number of electrons in the shell
1st	
2nd	
3rd	

Q5   **Complete** the table below showing the properties of the first 20 elements.   *(you will need the Periodic Table at the front of the book).*

Element	Symbol	Atomic Number	Mass Number	Number of Protons	Number of Electrons	Number of Neutrons	Electronic Configuration	Group Number
Hydrogen	H	1	1	1	1	0	1	—
Helium	He	2	4	2	2	2	2	0
Lithium	Li						2, 1	1
Beryllium								2
Boron				5				
Carbon								
Nitrogen		7						
Oxygen					8			
Fluorine							2, 7	
Neon								
Sodium		11						1
Magnesium								
Aluminium		13	27	13	13	14	2, 8, 3	3
Silicon								
Phosphorus								
Sulphur	S							
Chlorine								
Argon								
Potassium								
Calcium						20		2

Look at the table and answer these questions:

Q6   What is the link between **group number** and **number of outer electrons**?

Q7   What is the link between the **Noble gases** (group 0) and **full outer shells**?

Q8   *Iodine is in group 7* — **how many** electrons does it have in its outer electron shell?

Q9   *Silicon is in group 4* — **how many** electrons does it have in its outer electron shell?

Q10   *Xenon is in group 0* — **how many** electrons does it have in its outer electron shell?

Q11   The **number of electrons** in the outer shell governs which **property** of the element?

Q12   An atom of element X has two outer electrons that do not fill the outer shell.

    a) **Name** its *group.*

    b) Is it a **metal** or **non-metal**?

    c) Name **another** element with similar chemical properties to X.

Electron Arrangement

Q13   Give the **full electronic arrangement** in the following dot and cross diagrams.
(The first three have been done for you).

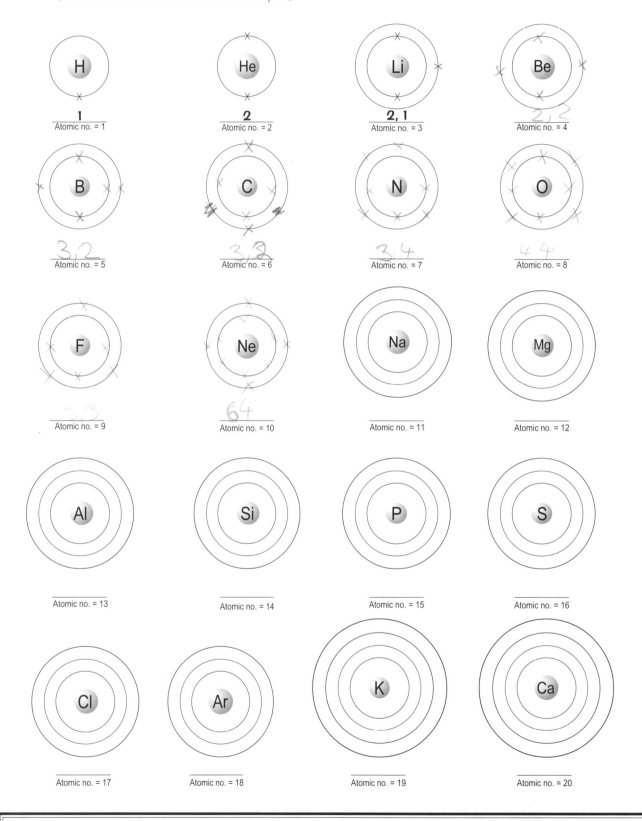

H
1
Atomic no. = 1

He
2
Atomic no. = 2

Li
2, 1
Atomic no. = 3

Be
2,2
Atomic no. = 4

B
3,2
Atomic no. = 5

C
3,3
Atomic no. = 6

N
3,4
Atomic no. = 7

O
4,4
Atomic no. = 8

F
Atomic no. = 9

Ne
6,4
Atomic no. = 10

Na
Atomic no. = 11

Mg
Atomic no. = 12

Al
Atomic no. = 13

Si
Atomic no. = 14

P
Atomic no. = 15

S
Atomic no. = 16

Cl
Atomic no. = 17

Ar
Atomic no. = 18

K
Atomic no. = 19

Ca
Atomic no. = 20

Top Tips: In Exams they're always asking you to draw out electronic **arrangements**, or "configurations" — just make sure you can work them out from **atomic numbers** or the **Periodic Table**. They might only ask you to draw the **outer shell** — easy or what......

Elements, Mixtures and Compounds

Q1 **Complete the table** by putting a tick in the correct column. The first one has been done for you.

Substance	Element	Mixture	Compound
Copper	✔		
Air			
Distilled water			
Brine			
Sodium			
Cupro-nickel			
Sodium chloride			
Copper sulphate			
Sulphur			
Oxygen			
Sea water			
Bronze			
Petrol			
Blue ink			
Steel			
Steam			
Milk			

Q2 In the boxes below **draw out circles** to represent atoms of elements and molecules of compounds.

A pure element

A mixture of two elements

A pure compound

A mixture of three compounds

A mixture of one element and one compound

Three atoms of one element

Two molecules of two different compounds

Three molecules of one compound, made of three atoms

Q3 Give a definition of a compound.

Q4 Give a definition of an element.

Q5 Give a definition of a mixture.

Ions

Answer these questions about ions:

Q1 What is an **ion**?

Q2 Give **two** examples of ions made from single atoms.

Q3 Give **two** examples of ions made from several atoms.

Q4 **Complete** this paragraph using the words provided:

-ve   protons   negatively charged   neutral   positively charged

Atoms are electrically _____ because they have equal numbers of _____ (+ve) and electrons (____). If electrons are taken away from a metal atom or hydrogen, then it becomes _____ _____ because it has less electrons than protons. If electrons are added to a non-metal atom, it becomes _____ _____ because it then has more electrons than protons.

Example 1: Positive Ions (metals and hydrogen)

SODIUM ION FROM SODIUM

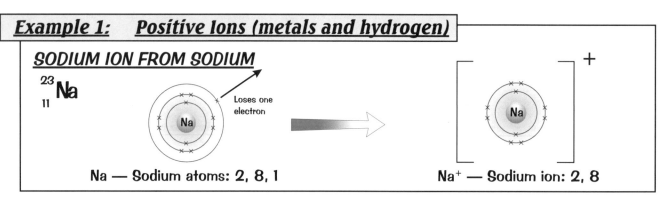

$^{23}_{11}Na$

Loses one electron

Na — Sodium atoms: 2, 8, 1

Na^+ — Sodium ion: 2, 8

Example 2: Negative Ions (non-metals)

OXIDE ION FROM OXYGEN

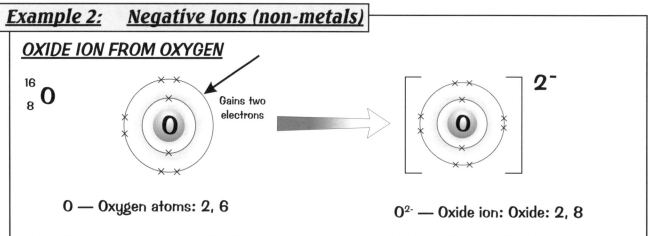

$^{16}_{8}O$

Gains two electrons

O — Oxygen atoms: 2, 6

O^{2-} — Oxide ion: Oxide: 2, 8

Q5 **Draw** the ions below exactly like those above.

(Remember Group I make 1 + ions and Group 2 make 2 +).
   a) Potassium.   **b)** Magnesium.   **c)** Calcium.   **d)** Aluminium.

Q6 **Draw** the ions below exactly like those above.

(Remember Group 7 make 1 - ions and group 6 make 2 -).
   a) Fluoride.   **b)** Chloride.   **c)** Sulphide.   **d)** Oxide.

Q7 What will be the **charge** on a **metal or hydrogen** ion? *(e.g. Groups 1, 2 and 3)*

Q8 What will be the charge on a **non-metal** ion? *(e.g. Groups 6 and 7)*

Ions

These questions cover all the basics of ionic bonding:

Q9 What is an ionic bond?

Q10 If an atom gains an electron, what charge does it have?

Q11 If an atom loses an electron, what charge does it have?

Q12 Why do sodium ions have a 1^+ charge?

Q13 Why do chloride ions have a 1^- charge?

Q14 What charge would you find on a Group 2 ion?

Q15 What charge would you find on a Group 6 ion?

Q16 Why do you think it is rare to find a 4^+ ion of carbon?

Q17 What is a cation and what is an anion?

Q18 **Draw** an electron configuration diagram to show what happens when a lithium atom reacts with a chlorine atom. Name the compound formed.

Q19 **Draw** an electron configuration diagram to show what happens when a magnesium atom reacts with two chlorine atoms.

Q20 Why is sodium chloride neutral?

Q21 **Draw** a picture to show the positions of sodium and chloride ions in a sodium chloride crystal.

Q22 Give the **formulae** of magnesium oxide, sodium fluoride, sodium oxide, magnesium sulphate and sodium sulphate, using the following:

Mg^{2+} $\qquad$ Na^+ $\qquad$ SO_4^{2-} $\qquad$ F^- $\qquad$ O^{2-}

Q23 **Name the following ions:**

a) Na^+ b) Cl^- c) S^{2-} d) NO_3^- e) SO_4^{2-} f) I^- g) F^- h) K^+ i) Ca^{2+} j) Mg^{2+} k) PO_4^{3-} l) H^+ m) Ba^{2+}

Q24 **Select from the list below:**

SO_4^{2-} $\qquad$ Mg^{2+} $\qquad$ Kr $\qquad$ MgO $\qquad$ CO_2

a) an example of a gas consisting of **single atoms**.

b) an example of a substance made from **ions**.

c) an example of a substance made from **molecules**.

d) an example of a compound.

e) an example of an **ion**.

f) an example of a **molecular ion** (compound ion).

Q25 **Which in the following list are general properties of an ionically bonded compound?**

a) High boiling point $\qquad$ d) Non-conductor when melted

b) Usually dissolve in water $\qquad$ e) Weak forces hold molecules together

c) Conductor when solid $\qquad$ f) Non-crystalline

Q26 If any of the properties listed in question 25 are not properties of ionically bonded compounds then correct them (*e.g. if they've not got a high boiling point they must have a low one*).

Top Tips: **Ionic** compounds are formed when electrons are **swapped** between one atom and another, to get that sought-after **full-outer-shell** feeling. Remember they contain a **metal** and a **non-metal** — and don't forget which ions are **positive** and which **negative**.

Covalent Bonding

Atoms join up to make <u>molecules</u>. They do this by forming chemical <u>bonds</u>. A chemical bond always involves <u>electrons</u>. A covalent bond is one where atoms <u>share</u> one or more pairs of electrons. This means that both the atoms can effectively have a <u>full shell</u>. A full shell is a more stable arrangement of electrons, like that of a noble gas. Noble gases are <u>inert</u> and <u>very stable</u>. In summary, atoms undergo chemical reactions to attain a <u>full shell</u>, which makes them <u>more stable</u> — and that's why atoms react to make compounds...

Got all that, then you can answer these:

Q1   What is a **molecule?**

Q2   Give **another** name for the joining of two atoms together.

Q3   A covalent bond involves two atoms sharing what?

Q4   Draw two crosses on these circles to represent the electrons in a single covalent bond:

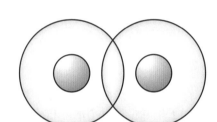

Q5   Why do atoms **share** electrons?

Q6   Which group of the periodic table do the atoms "try to be like"?

Q7   **Write out and draw** the electron configuration of neon:

Q8   **Write out** the electron configuration of chlorine.

Q9   **How many more** electrons does chlorine need in order to have a "noble gas" configuration (a full outer shell)?

Q10 Using the diagram opposite, **draw out** the electron arrangement in a chlorine molecule.
(Draw outer shells only).

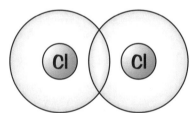

H Q11   Which of the following list are **general properties** of simple molecular substances?

   a) Low boiling point.

   b) Soluble in water.

   c) Conductor when melted.

   d) Non-conductor when solid.

   e) Weak forces attract molecules to each other.

   f) Crystalline.

H Q12 If any of the properties listed in question 11 are not properties of simple molecular substances then **correct them.**
   (e.g. if they've not got a low boiling point then they must have a high one).

Covalent Bonding

Q13 **Draw out** the following dot and cross diagrams — showing the outer shells only (use the Periodic Table on the inside cover if needed).

a) Hydrogen (H_2):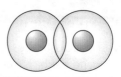

b) Water (H_2O):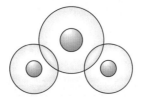

c) Ammonia (NH_3):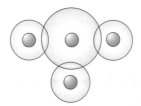

d) Methane (CH_4):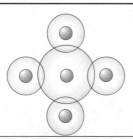

e) Chlorine (Cl_2):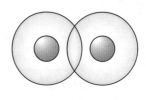

Q14 A single covalent bond involves sharing a pair of electrons.

What does a **double covalent bond** involve?

Q15 What is the **full electronic configuration** of oxygen?

Q16 How many **more** electrons does oxygen need in order to fill its outer shell?

Q17 **Which element** has the electron configuration 2,8?

Q18 Oxygen can attain a full shell by forming a double bond with itself.

Using dots and crosses fill in the double bond to the right and label it. Then fill in the other electrons.

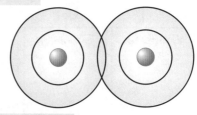

Q19 Carbon dioxide has the formula CO_2 — drawn out in the diagram below.

Fill in the electrons in the **outer shells** of the oxygen and carbon atoms.

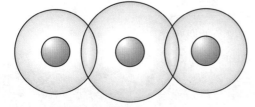

Q20 **Fill in** the electron configuration for the molecule of ethene (C_2H_4) shown here:

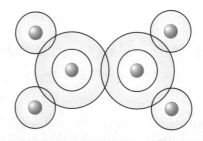

Top Tips: You need to know **all** the examples on this page for a high grade — especially the molecules with double bonds. Just remember atoms "like" to have a **full outer shell**, so some atoms will **share electrons** so that they *"feel"* like they've got a full outer shell.

Structures

Q1   Below is a diagram that classifies substances according to their structures.

   a) Write in the missing words in the *"structure"* boxes.

   b) The substances **in the box below** can be split into groups:
   write each in the correct *"example"* box in the diagram.

> Cupro-nickel   C   KI   Mg SO_2 PCl_3 Zn
>
> I_2 C_2H_4 HCl O_2 Ca CO_2 KCl SiO_2
>
> Cu S_8 P_5 NaCl $CuSO_4$ Bronze

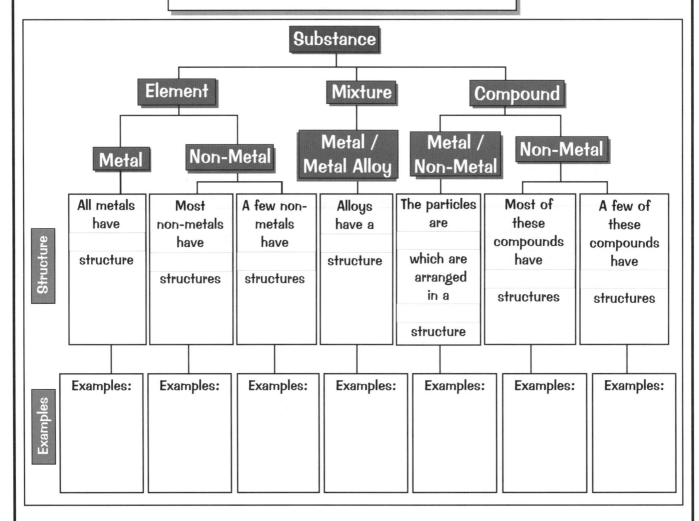

Q2   "Substances have physical properties because of their chemical properties".

   Explain what this means and state whether or not you agree with it.

Q3   **Why** are ionic substances generally brittle?

Q4   Why do most covalent substances **melt easily**?

Q5   **Which** covalent substances do not melt easily?

Q6   Why do ionic substances only **conduct electricity**
   when molten or when dissolved in water?

Q7   Referring to the diagram opposite, **explain** why
   ionic crystals dissolve in water.

Metals and Metallic Bonding

H Q1   Describe how an atom of iron joins up to other atoms in an iron bar.

H Q2   *Metals have "giant structures of atoms".* What is a **giant structure**?

H Q3   What are **"free electrons"**, and where do they originate?

H Q4   **Draw** a diagram to show the metal ions and free electrons in a giant structure.

H Q5   Look at the table opposite:

a) Complete the table.

b) *Metals have the properties shown in the table because of their bonding.*
   What is the **name** given to a bond in a metal?

Answer these alloy questions.

H Q6   What is an alloy?

H Q7   Why do we **use** metal alloys?

Metal Property	Good Example	Reason	Exception (if any)
Strong			
Good Conductor of Heat			
Good Conductor of electricity			
Can be rolled into sheets (malleable)			
Can be drawn into wires (ductile)			

H Q8   Look at the diagram below. **Explain** why the alloy is **stronger** than the pure metal.

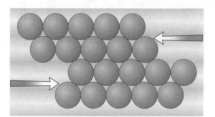

Pure Metal

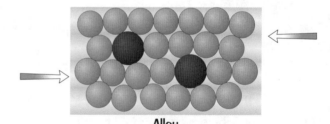

Alloy

Metal	Melting Point (°C)	Boiling Point (°C)	Specific Heat Capacity (J/Kg/°C)	Density (g/cm³)	Electrical Conductivity (S/m)	Reaction with Water
A	659	2447	900	2.7	0.41	none
B	1083	2582	390	8.9	0.64	none
C	1539	2887	470	7.9	0.11	slight
D	328	1751	130	11.3	0.05	none
E	98	890	1222	0.97	0.20	very reactive
F	183	2500	130	7.3	0.66	none
G	1063	2707	129	19.3	0.49	none
H	3377	5527	135	19.3	0.20	none

H Q9   Use the information above to choose a suitable metal for each of the following uses:

In all cases **explain** your **answers**:

a) A filament for a **household light bulb**.

b) A metal that could be used to make **solder**.

c) A metal used to make **aeroplanes**.

d) A coolant for a **nuclear reactor**.

e) An overhead **power cable**.

Hazards

Q1 **Link up** the hazchem symbols with their description, and write in an example of each:

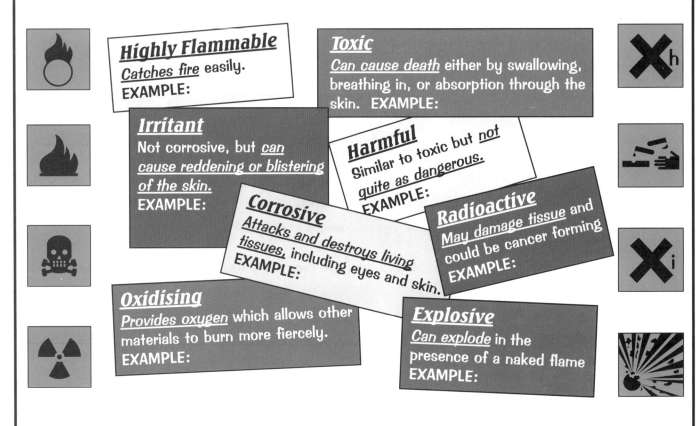

Q2 Why do we have a system of hazchem symbols, and why are they pictures, not just words?

Q3 **Describe** how you would handle a "corrosive chemical".

Q4 Look at the following information from the side of a chemical tanker.

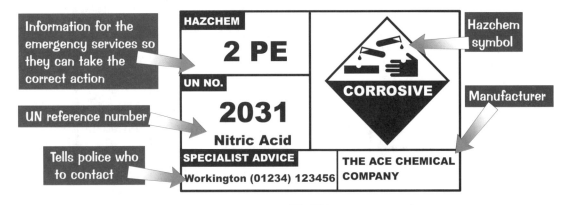

a) Why does the information have a **hazchem symbol**?

b) Why might the emergency services require **more** information than just the hazchem symbol?

c) Why is a **phone number** always included?

d) A tanker overturns in a crowded shopping area, but doesn't crack open. The Hazchem label tells the emergency services that its contents are corrosive, requiring full body protection when handled, but that they can be washed down the drains. Write a **short summary** of the important steps a fire officer handling this tanker should take.

Crude Oil

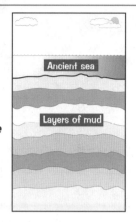

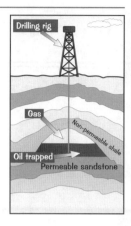

Oil and natural gas have formed from the remains of plants and sea creatures. They are the result of the action of heat and pressure on plant and animal remains over millions of years, in the absence of air.

Oil and gas rise up through permeable rocks and become trapped under impermeable rocks. They are then extracted by drilling.

In the exploration for oil, Geologists carry out test drilling to check for the rock formations that trap oil.

Most wells are 1000 — 5000m deep, but some can reach down 8km. Most of the oil is at high pressure, so is easily removed. But some deposits require water to be pumped down to force the oil out. Oil is transported in tankers or piped to a refinery where the mixture is separated.

Answer the following questions:

Q1 **Explain** in your own words how crude oil has formed.

Q2 What is a **mixture**?

Q3 Crude oil is a **mixture** of what?

Q4 What is a **hydrocarbon**?

Q5 Why is the oil known as "**crude**" oil?

Q6 **Why** is crude oil of little use without refining?

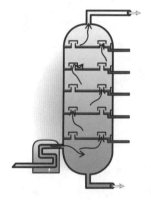

Q7 **How** is crude oil transported to the refinery?

Q8 **Name** another method of transporting oil, not mentioned above.

Q9 Why are **oil spills** a problem to the environment?

Q10 Oil is **non-renewable**. What does this **mean**?

Q11 Give three **advantages** and three **disadvantages** of burning oil products.

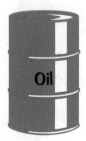

Top Tips: Oil is important — as a **fuel** and as a **resource** to make other useful things from. More importantly for you — it'll be in the exam, so you need to know **how oil forms**, what it's **used for** and what **environmental** problems oil spillages and burning oil products cause.

Fractional Distillation

Q1   What is a fossil fuel?

Q2   Complete the diagram below by filling in labels A to E with the correct fraction.

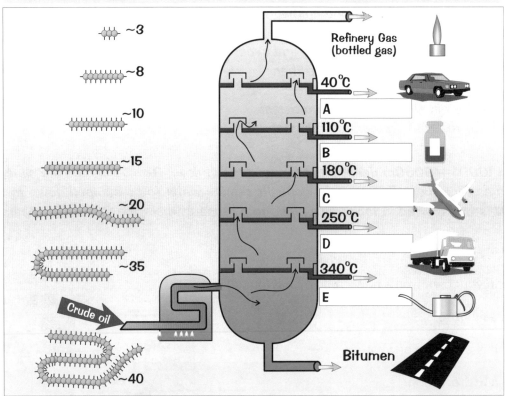

Q3   What do the following terms mean?

a) Volatile   **b)** Flammable   **c)** Refining

d) Boils off   **e)** Fraction   **f)** Distillation

g) Viscous   **h)** Refinery gas   **i)** Carbon chain

Q4   How does the boiling point of a hydrocarbon change as its carbon chain length increases?

Q5   Describe how the fractional distillation of crude oil works.

Q6   Why is crude oil so important?

Q7   How does the flammability of a hydrocarbon change as its carbon chain length increases?

Q8   How does the volatility of a hydrocarbon change its carbon chain length increases?

Q9   Which would flow more easily — a hydrocarbon composed of short carbon chains or long carbon chains?

Q10   Which fractions will ignite most easily — short carbon chains or long carbon chains?

Oil is a finite resource:

Q11   What does finite mean?

Q12   What could you do to make oil last longer?

Q13   What could all nations do to make oil last longer?

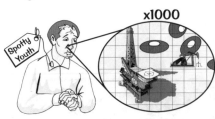

Hydrocarbons

*If a liquid is quite "thick" and takes a long time to run down a slope, we say it is "viscous".
We can measure how long it takes for a certain amount of liquid to run through a burette,
and this will indicate how viscous the liquid is.
Lubricating oils in car engines keep moving metal surfaces apart. Viscous oils do this better
than runny oils; but if they are too viscous they don't lubricate the moving parts properly.*

The following experiment was set up to find which of two oils was the most viscous.

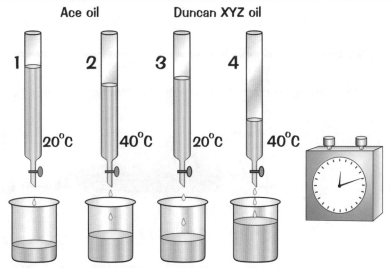

The time taken for the oil to run through the burette was noted at two temperatures.

Burette	Temperature / °C	Time for 50 cm³ of oil to flow through / s
1	20	90
2	40	53
3	20	64
4	40	28

Use the table to answer the following questions:

Q1　Draw a bar chart of the above information.

Q2　Which oil is most viscous at 20°C?

Q3　Which oil is the most viscous at 40°C?

Q4　Temperatures in an engine are much higher than 40°C. What will happen to the viscosity of these oils at engine temperature?

Q5　How could you improve the experiment to prove which oil was the most viscous when used in an engine?

Q6　If you were designing an engine oil, would you use short chain or long chain hydrocarbons?

Q7　What might happen to very viscous oil on a very cold morning?

Q8　At one time in cold weather, lorry drivers would warm their diesel tanks by making a small fire under the tank.

a) Why do you think they did this?

b) What problems might occur doing this?

c) Additives are now put in diesel oil, but not all year round. Why aren't they always put in?

Hydrocarbons

Q9   What is **cracking?**

Q10   **Give two reasons** why it is carried out.

Q11   Look at the diagram to the right.

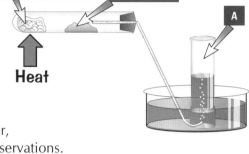

Rocksil wool soaked in paraffin

Al_2O_3 (catalyst)

A

Heat

   a) **Name** two conditions that are needed to crack paraffin.

   b) **Gas A produced in this reaction is an alkene.** What is an alkene?

   c) Alkenes are **unsaturated.** What does this mean?

   d) Paraffin does not decolourise orange/brown bromine water, but gas "**A**" collected in the gas jar does. **Explain** these observations.

H **e)** **Complete** the equation by filling in the box with the structural formula of A:

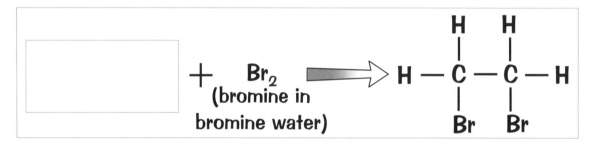

$$+ \quad Br_2 \quad \Longrightarrow$$

(bromine in bromine water)

   f) Name gas "**A**".

H **Q12**   Only the **larger** fractions obtained by the distillation of crude oil are cracked. Why is this?

H **Q13** $C_{16}H_{34}$ was heated strongly with a catalyst, in the absence of air. This is one reaction that occurred:

$$C_{16}H_{34} \rightarrow 2C_2H_4 + C_6H_{12} + C_6H_{14}$$

   a) **Name** the process shown in the equation.

   b) Which of these molecules are unsaturated?

   c) Which of them are saturated?

   d) Which molecules would:

     i) Decolourise bromine water?

     ii) Polymerise?

   e) Why is this reaction carried out in the absence of air?

   f) **Complete the dot and cross diagram** opposite, showing the outer electrons in an ethene molecule.

   g) **Name** two uses of "cracked" hydrocarbons.

   h) What is made when many molecules of ethene join up?

   i) If ethene reacts with chlorine, chloroethene is produced. **Name** the molecule that forms when chloroethene polymerises — and give its abbreviation.

Top Tips:
We break up long hydrocarbons to make them **less viscous**, and more importantly to produce **alkenes**. If you take a long hydrocarbon, and make a shorter one out of it, the bit left over **has** to be an alkene, 'cos otherwise there aren't enough bonds to go round. Remember alkenes have a C = C **double bond**, and they join up to make **polymers** — cracking stuff.

Alkanes

H Q1   Complete the table by filling in the missing information:

Alkanes = C_nH_{2n+2}

Name	Formula	Number of Carbons	Melting Point(°C)	Boiling Point(°C)	Structural Formula
Methane	CH_4	1	-182	-164	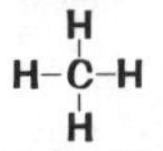 H H–C–H H
Ethane	C_2H_6		-183	-89	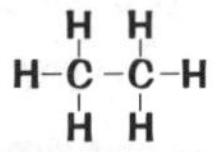 H H H–C–C–H H H
Propane	C_3H_8	3	-190	-42	
Butane	C_4H_{10}	4	-138	0	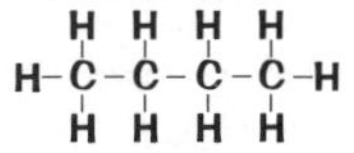 H H H H H–C–C–C–C–H H H H
Pentane	C_5H_{12}	5	-130	36	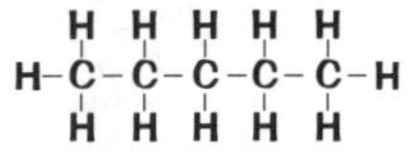 H H H H H H–C–C–C–C–C–H H H H H
Hexane		6	-95	69	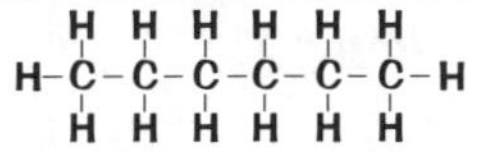 H H H H H H H–C–C–C–C–C–C–H H H H H H
Heptane	C_7H_{16}	7	-91	99	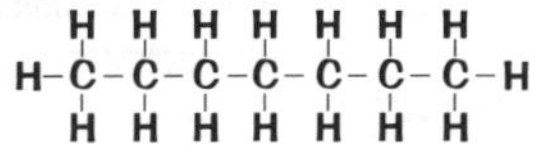 H H H H H H H H–C–C–C–C–C–C–C–H H H H H H H
Octane		8	-57	126	
Nonane	C_9H_{20}	9	-51	151	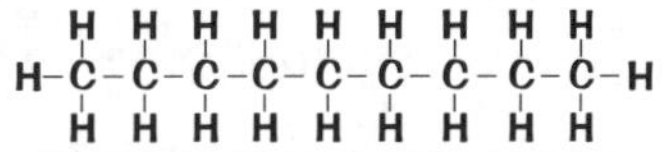 H H H H H H H H H H–C–C–C–C–C–C–C–C–C–H H H H H H H H H
Decane	$C_{10}H_{22}$		-30	174	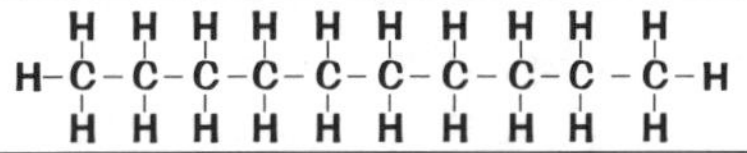 H H H H H H H H H H H–C–C–C–C–C–C–C–C–C–C–H H H H H H H H H H

Use the table to help answer the following questions:

H Q2   **Draw a graph** using the above information, with the number of carbon atoms on the horizontal axis and boiling point on the vertical axis.

H Q3   Which alkanes are: **a)** solid   **b)** liquid   **c)** gas   ...at room temperature (25°C)?

H Q4   What is the link between the boiling point of alkanes and the number of carbons they have?

H Q5   Why should a compound with heavy and long molecules have a different boiling point from a compound with light and small molecules?

H Q6   **Estimate** the boiling point of $C_{11}H_{24}$.

H Q7   **Draw out** dot and cross diagrams for the first five alkanes. Methane has been done for you below:

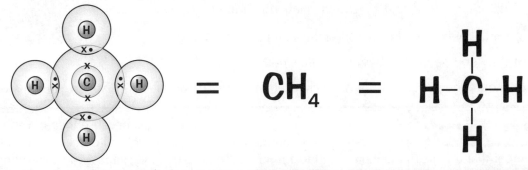

Alkanes

Alkanes are organic compounds that form a homologous series of hydrocarbons. They only contain single covalent bonds and are therefore saturated hydrocarbons. They form 3D molecules but are usually drawn flat. They have the general formula C_nH_{2n+2}. They do not decolourise bromine water and they burn cleanly to produce carbon dioxide and water.

Answer the following:

H Q8   **Explain** what is meant by a "**single covalent bond**".

H Q9   What does the term "**saturated**" mean?

H Q10   Explain why alkanes **do not react** with bromine water.

H Q11   **Complete** the following equations and balance them:

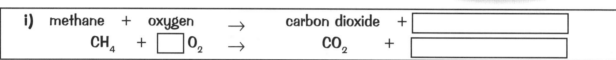

i)   methane + oxygen → carbon dioxide + ☐

    CH_4 + ☐ O_2 → CO_2 + ☐

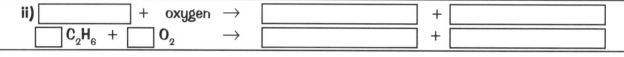

ii) ☐ + oxygen → ☐ + ☐

☐ C_2H_6 + ☐ O_2 → ☐ + ☐

iii) propane + oxygen → ☐ + ☐

☐ + ☐ O_2 → ☐ + ☐

H Q12   Why is it dangerous to burn alkanes in a limited oxygen supply?

H Q13   Alkanes are unreactive and will not polymerise (join up to make molecules). **Explain**, using examples, why this is so.

H Q14   A catalyst can be used to break down long alkane molecule chains into smaller, more useful molecules. What is the **name** of this process?

H Q15   Why does it make more sense to turn unreactive alkanes into **more useful chemicals**, rather than **burn** them?

H Q16   State **uses** for methane, propane, butane and octane.

H Q17   Pure methane has no smell. Below are three molecules used to give methane a smell.

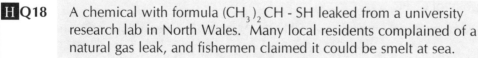

$CH_3CH_2 - SH$ $(CH_3)_3C - SH$ $CH_3CH_2 - S - CH_2CH_3$

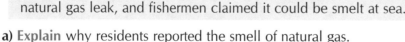

Why do you think this is done?

H Q18   A chemical with formula $(CH_3)_2CH - SH$ leaked from a university research lab in North Wales. Many local residents complained of a natural gas leak, and fishermen claimed it could be smelt at sea.

a) Explain why residents reported the smell of natural gas.

b) Why do you think fishermen could smell the gas **at sea**?

c) Should the gas authorities have checked **all** of these complaints? **Explain** your answer.

Top Tips: Alkanes hardly undergo any actual reactions because they haven't got any spare bonds to do things with — **combustion** and **cracking** are the main ones. Remember that and learn the **names** and **formulae** of the alkanes in Q1, and you'll be rolling in marks.

Alkenes

H Q1   Alkenes are unsaturated hydrocarbons.

a) What do you understand by the term **unsaturated**?

b) Why does this make alkenes **useful**?

H Q2   Below is a table showing some properties of the alkenes. Use this to **answer** the questions.

Alkene	Melting Point °C	Boiling Point °C	State at RTP
Ethene	-168.9	-103.6	Gas
Propene	-185.1	-47.3	Gas
But-1-ene	-185.2	-6.2	Gas
Pent-1-ene	-138	30	Liquid

a) Comment on any trends you can see in the:
   i) melting points   **ii)** boiling points   **iii)** states at room temperature and pressure.

b) Estimate the melting and boiling points of the next two alkenes.
   Give reasons for your answer.

c) Explain these trends you mentioned in part **a)**.

H Q3   The general formula for the alkenes is C_nH_{2n}.

a) **Explain** what this general formula means.

b) The structural formula for ethene is shown to the right.
   i) Write the molecular formula for ethene.
   ii) Propene has a formula C_3H_6. **Draw** the structural formula for propene.

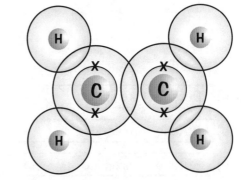

H Q4   Elements are easily added to alkenes. These reactions are called **addition reactions**.

a) **Why** do alkenes so readily undergo addition reactions?

b) Ethene can undergo an addition reaction with hydrogen.
   i) Write an equation to show this reaction.
   ii) Draw the structural formulae of the molecules in this reaction.
   iii) What is the name of the **product** formed?

H Q5   The formula for the alkene, ethene, is C_2H_4.

a) **Complete** the dot and cross diagram of ethene to show
   the bonding (note $^{12}_{6}C$ and $^{1}_{1}H$):

b) How is this molecule **different** from
   a molecule of ethane?

H Q6   Alkenes burn readily in oxygen.

a) What products would you expect from the **burning of ethene** in air?

b) Write a **balanced** equation to show the **products formed** when ethene burns in air.

c) **Write** a **word equation** to show what would happen when propene was burnt in air.

d) They tend to burn with a sooty flame. What might cause the **soot**?

Alkenes

H Q7 **Bromine water** can be used to distinguish between ethane and ethene.

What happens when: **i)** ethene **ii)** ethane ...is mixed with bromine water?

Bromine Water

H Q8 **Complete** the table below.

Hint: 'but-' means 2, 'pent-' means five,'hex-' means six and 'hept-' means seven.

Alkene	No. of Carbon atoms	Formula	Structural Formula
Butene			
Pentene			
Hexene			
Heptene			

H Q9 Ethene is referred to as a monomer.

a) What do you understand by the term *"monomer"*?

b) Ethene molecules add together to form a very long chain. What is this reaction called?

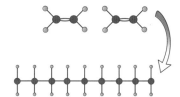

H Q10 "Ethene is a product of crude oil."

a) Is this statement true or false? **Give reasons** for your answer.

b) Why is ethene so important industrially?

Oil

H Q11 Complete these equations:

a) Butene + oxygen $\rightarrow$

b) Butene + chlorine $\rightarrow$ dichloro_____

c) Butene + bromine $\rightarrow$ dibromo_____

d) Propene + oxygen $\rightarrow$

Top Tips: Alkenes are **unsaturated** (have double bonds) — **spare bonds ready**, to **react** with other chemicals or make **polymers.** It makes them a bit more exciting than alkanes but you've still got to learn the **names** and **structural formulae**, and get an idea of the **physical properties**.

Polymers and Plastics

H **Q1**   **Explain** what you understand by the term *"polymerisation"*.

H **Q2**   Ethene can undergo many addition reactions to form long chain polymers.

a) What **reaction conditions** are necessary for this to happen?
b) **Why** are these conditions needed?

H **Q3**   Lots of ethene molecules can join together to form a substance that is useful.

a) What is this polymer **called**?

b) Using the ethene molecule to help you, **draw** a diagram to show how the monomers of ethene form their polymer.

c) **Explain** the naming of ethene's polymer.

d) Why is ethene the **starting point** for many plastics?

$$\begin{array}{ccc} H & & H \\ \diagdown & & \diagup \\ & C = C & \\ \diagup & & \diagdown \\ H & & H \end{array}$$

Q4   Using the information given in the first table below, decide which polymer you think would be **most suitable** for the jobs below. Fill your answers in the second table:

We bring you Gold, Frankincense... and poly-myrrh

Polymer	Some properties
1) Polystyrene	Cheap, easily moulded, can be expanded into foam.
2) Polythene	Cheap, strong, easy to mould.
3) Polypropene	Forms strong fibres, highly elastic.
4) PTFE	Hard, waxy, things do not stick to it.
5) Perspex	Transparent, easily moulded, does not easily shatter.

Job	Plastic	Reason
a) Hot food container		
b) Plastic bags		
c) Carpet		
d) Picnic glasses		
e) Buckets		
f) Ropes		
g) Bubble packing		
h) Insulating material		
i) Yoghurt cartons		
j) Non-stick frying pans		

Polymers and Plastics

H Q5 **Complete** the paragraph below by filling in the missing words.

ethene monomers	monomer ethene	carbon	catalyst	polythene	polymerisation
double bond	monomer	polymer	plastics	addition	saturated	high pressure

_____ is the formation of long chain _____ molecules from the _____ of single

monomer units. The type of molecules in the _____ give the _____ its properties.

_____ are made from these long chain hydrocarbons. _____ is made from the

_____. _____ are brought together at _____

over a heated _____. The _____ is broken forming a _____ molecule.

H Q6 Other alkenes can also break their double bond to form long-chain polymers.

For each monomer given in the table below, **draw** what you would expect its polymer to look like, then **name** the polymer.

Monomer	Polymer	Name
a) H H C = C H CH₃		
b) H H C = C H ⬡		
c) Cl H C = C H H		

Q7 Sort the following into a list of the **good** and **bad** points of using plastics.

Fairly cheap   Can catch fire   Low density

Can be coloured   Insulators   Moulded easily

Not affected by acids or alkalis   May produce toxic gases when burnt

Non-degradable   Can be very strong   Difficult to dispose of

---

Top Tips: Polymerisation uses a **catalyst** and a bit of **pressure** to get alkenes to open up their **double bonds** and **join up** — almost the opposite of cracking. These polymers are loads **more useful** than the hydrocarbon they came from — and the **length** of the polymer can be controlled to **tailor-make** the molecule for a particular job. If that's not exciting I don't know what is.

Section Two — Changing Materials   *AQA Syllabus*

Metal Ores

Q1 What is a metal **ore**?

Q2 **Give** an example of a metal ore.

Q3 In what form are very **unreactive** metals found in the ground?

Q4 **Give 3 examples** of metals found naturally in the ground.

Q5 In what form are **reactive metals** found in the ground?

Q6 The diagram below shows some of the processes involved in **extracting a metal** from its ore. **Match** each picture **a) - f)** with the correct expression from the following box:

Pure metal   Carbon reduction   Earth containing ore dug from ground   Electrolysis
Metal ore detected in ground   Waste earth removed to concentrate ore

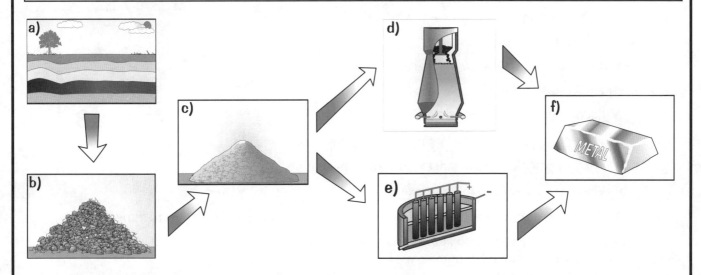

Q7 List each metal in the box under the correct **method of extraction**.

Thermal decomposition of ore	Reduction of metal ore with Carbon	Electrolysis of molten ore	Metals occur naturally

Iron   Copper   Potassium   Magnesium   Aluminium
Silver   Zinc   Sodium   Lead   Calcium   Gold

Q8 Look at the table opposite.

a) **Draw a bar chart** showing abundance of the metals.

b) **What does** "abundant" mean?

c) Which is the **most abundant** metal listed?

d) Name a **scarce** metal.

e) Was the most abundant metal the first to be **extracted**?

H f) What is the relationship between the **reactivity** of the metal and the date it was first **extracted**?

Metal	Date first extracted	% Abundance in the Earth's crust
Aluminium	1827	8.1
Calcium	1808	3.6
Copper	Ancient time	<1.0
Gold	Ancient time	<1.0
Iron	Ancient time (Iron age)	5.0
Potassium	1807	2.6

Extracting Iron — The Blast Furnace

Q1   Iron can be extracted from its ore in a Blast Furnace.

a) **Explain why** iron can be extracted in this way, but sodium
   and aluminium have to be extracted by electrolysis.

b) What is the **name** of the most common iron ore used?

c) What element is the **iron bonded** to in this ore?

d) What is the **formula** of this ore?

Q2   The diagram shows a section through a blast furnace.

a) Which **three solids** are put into the blast furnace?

b) Why is **hot air** blasted into the furnace?

c) Why does the temperature need to be as hot as **1500°C**?

d) What would you find at **A** and **B** in the diagram?

Q3   The first stage makes the gas carbon dioxide.

a) **How** is carbon dioxide produced?

b) **Write an equation** to show the reaction.

Q4   The next step:
   What does the **carbon dioxide** do in the blast furnace?

Q5   The final step involves changing the iron oxide into iron.

a) **Write an equation** and balance it to show what happens.

b) What has happened to the **iron oxide**?

c) Write an ionic equation to show the reaction in **a)** **(for example:** Fe^{3+} + *something* → *etc).*

d) i) In what **state** is the iron at the end of the reaction?
   ii) How is it **removed** from the blast furnace?

Q6   In all chemical processes it is important to remove the impurities, to leave a pure product.

a) What is the main **impurity** mixed with the ore?

b) Calcium Carbonate helps to remove this impurity, but first it needs to decompose.
   Complete the equation showing this decomposition:

$$CaCO_3 \rightarrow \rule{2cm}{0.4pt} + \rule{2cm}{0.4pt}$$

c) **Complete the equation** showing the formation of slag:

$$CaO + SiO_2 \rightarrow \rule{2cm}{0.4pt}$$

d) What can this **slag** be used for?

Q7   **Explain why** use of the blast furnace makes iron cheaper than a lot of other metals.

Q8   Iron can exist in two forms: iron(III) and iron(II).
   Complete the table opposite showing the
   differences between the two forms of iron oxide.
   (Relative atomic masses: Iron = 56, Oxygen = 16)

	Iron(III) oxide	Iron(II) oxide
Formula		
Ion Formed	Fe^{3+}	
Relative formula mass of compound		

Q9   Give **two** uses of iron.

Q10   a) **Name** one other metal that could be extracted by reduction from its oxide by coke.

b) **Why** is it difficult to extract magnesium by reduction with coke?

Top Tips:
Metals are all pretty useful, but they tend to occur in the ground as ores.
Don't forget, the way we **extract** them depends on **how reactive** they are.
You need to know the **blast furnace** process for **iron** extraction, it often comes up in the Exam.

Extracting Aluminium

Q1 Fill in the missing **arrows** from the labels on the diagram:

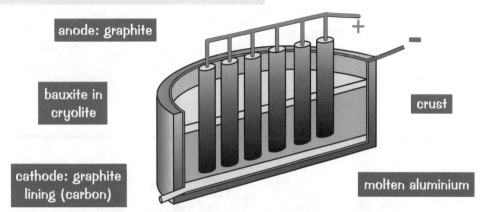

anode: graphite

bauxite in cryolite

crust

cathode: graphite lining (carbon)

molten aluminium

Q2 **Complete** the sentences using the following words:

reactive	aluminium	ore	difficult	Al
O_2	bauxite	900°C		cryolite

Aluminium is much more _____ than carbon so is extracted from its _____ using electrolysis. Aluminium is the most abundant metal in the Earth's crust, and is joined up with other elements, rock and clays, which make it _____ to extract. The ore of aluminium is called _____ which is impure aluminium oxide. It is purified, then dissolved in molten _____ (another ore of aluminium) which lowers the melting point from over 2000°C to about _____°C. Electricity passes through the melted ore separating the _____ from the oxygen.

The overall equation is: $2Al_2O_{3(l)} \rightarrow 4$ _____ $_{(l)} + 3$ _____ $_{(g)}$

Q3 Why must the bauxite be **purified** before it undergoes electrolysis?

Q4 Why is **cryolite** added?

Q5 **Give two reasons** why adding cryolite is such a good idea.

H Q6 **Write out** the reactions that take place at the cathode and at the anode:

At the cathode (-ve):

$Al^{3+} + 3$ _____ $\rightarrow$ _____

At the anode (+ve):

$2O^{2-} \rightarrow$ _____ $+ 4$ _____

H Q7 At **which** electrode does **a)** Reduction **b)** Oxidation ...take place?

H Q8 Why do the carbon rods have to be replaced from time to time?

H Q9 **Write out** a **word equation** for the reaction that uses up the carbon of the electrode.

Copper

Copper can be purified by electrolysis.

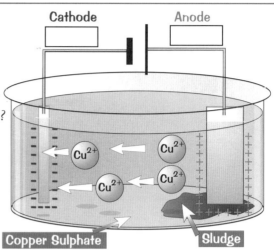

Cathode   **Anode**

Copper Sulphate   **Sludge**

Q1   Mark (+) and (-) on the battery.

Q2   Copper metal in the impure anode becomes copper ions Cu²⁺. Why do they travel towards the **cathode**?

Q3   What do the copper ions **accept** when they reach the cathode?

Q4   **Write** an equation to show this.

Q5   **Write** an equation to show what happens at the anode.

Q6   **Complete** the following paragraph using the words in the box. You can use them once, more than once or not at all.

purify	positive	splitting	electrolyte	sludge	electrolysis
anode	electricity	electrons	copper	anode	copper metal

_____ is the _____ of a compound by passing _____ through it. It is used to

_____ metals. _____ can be purified in this way. Copper sulphate solution is the

_____, which produces _____ ions and sulphate ions.

The impure copper is attached to the _____ electrode, the _____. This produces

_____ ions which are attracted to the negative cathode. Here they each gain _____ to

become _____ metal. A _____ from the impure _____ forms underneath the

_____.

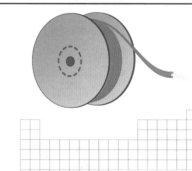

Q7   Why is copper **more resistant** to corrosion than metals like iron?

Q8   Why is copper so useful for **electrical wiring** in a house?

Q9   **Give two** other uses of copper.

Q10   **Name two** alloys of copper.

Q11   In what **part** of the Periodic Table do you find copper?

Q12   Would you expect copper compounds to be **white** or **coloured**?

Q13   What **physical property** of copper makes it a suitable material for pans?

Q14   Does copper react with dilute mineral acids like hydrochloric acid or sulphuric acid? **Explain** your answer.

Q15   Lithium is a metal that floats on water. Does copper float on water? **Explain** your answer.

Top Tips: You **get** copper out of copper ore by **reduction**, copper is **purified** by electrolysis. Remember that, learn the diagram and information in Question 1, remember **which** electrode the **impure copper** is — and you'll be all set to get **loads of juicy marks.**

Uses of Metals

Q1   People who badly break a leg or an ankle often have a pin placed in their leg to help the bones heal — they hold the bones in place and add strength to them while they are healing.

The table below lists some materials that could be used as a pin.

Material	Strength	Reactivity	Cost	Hardness	Density	Toughness
Titanium	H	L	H	H	H	H
Mild Steel	H	H	L	H	H	H
Aluminium	M	M	M	M	M	M
Ceramic	VH	L	L	VH	L	L

L = Low   M = Medium   H = High   VH = Very High

a) Does the pin need to be **strong**? Yes

b) Just looking at the strength column — **which example** would you choose for a pin? Mild steel

c) Does the pin need to be **reactive**? Yes

d) Just looking at the reactivity column — **which example** would you choose for a pin? Mild steel

e) Does the pin need to be **cheap**? Yes

f) Just looking at the cost column — **which example** would you choose for a pin? Mild steel,

g) Does the pin need to be **hard**? Yep

h) Just looking at the hardness column — **which example** would you choose for a pin? Mild steel

i) Does the pin need to be **dense**? Yes

j) Just looking at the density column — **which example** would you choose for a pin? mild steel

k) After examining **all** of the information, **explain** in as much detail as possible which material you would choose for a pin to place in broken bones. ceramic

Q2   Look at the information in the table below. R, S, T, and U are all metals. **Explain** in as much detail as possible which material would be most suitable to use to build an **aeroplane body**.

Material	Strength	Cost (£)	Density (g/cm³)	Melting Point (°C)
R	High	100	3.0	1000
S	Medium	90.0	9.0	150
T	High	450	8.0	1200
U	Low	200	11.0	1070

Uses of Metals

Q3   The table below lists many properties of metals.

Complete the table by filling in for each property two appropriate examples, an exception, and a use. One has been done for you.

Property (Quality)	Give two examples	Give an exception to rule (if possible)	What is this quality useful for?
Metals are solid	Iron Copper	Mercury	Used in the construction of buildings
Metals are hard			
Metals are strong (have high tensile strength)			
Metals are shiny			
Metals bend			
Metals are tough (difficult to break)			
Metals usually feel cold (conduct heat well)			
Metals conduct electricity well			
Metals are dense (heavy for their size)			
Some metals are magnetic (are attracted to magnetic poles)			
Metals are sonorous (make a nice noise when struck)			
Metals expand when heated			
Metals react with the oxygen in the air			
Metals react with acids			

Top Tips: Most of these properties are down to the special **metallic bond** . You've got to make sure you can **list** all of those metallic properties and say **why** they're useful. Questions where you have to **choose** a metal for a job are very common. So, **learn those properties**.

Ammonia and Fertilisers

Q1   Why is the Haber Process **so important**?

Q2   The two gases used to make ammonia in the Haber Process are hydrogen and nitrogen.

    a) Where does the nitrogen come from?

    b) Where does the hydrogen come from?

Q3   Look at the diagram opposite.

    a) Why is the iron catalyst on **large trays**?

    b) How does this **affect** the reaction?

    c) What is the **function** of the condenser?

    d) Why is the reaction at a temperature of **450°C** and a pressure of **200** atmospheres?

    e) How would a **very low temperature** affect the rate of this reaction?

    f) | Nitrogen + Hydrogen $\rightleftharpoons$ Ammonia. |

      i) Write this equation in **symbols** and balance it.

      ii) What does the symbol " $\rightleftharpoons$ " mean?

    g) Not all the nitrogen and hydrogen that enter end up as Ammonia.

    Why is this and **how** is it compensated for?

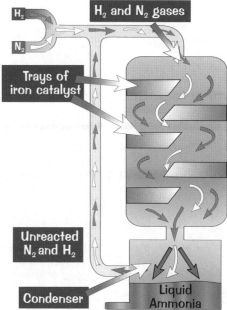

Pressure 200 atmospheres
Temperature 450 °C
Catalyst iron

H Q4   The production of ammonia on an industrial scale needs to be economical. The temperature and pressure can be chosen to maximise the yield.

    Explain why the reaction is **not** carried out at even **higher pressures** when this would increase the yield more.

Q5   **Complete** the following paragraphs by filling in the missing words from the list below. The words may be used once, more than once or not at all.

| 450 | 1000 | ammonia | molecule | hydrogen | nitrogen | molecules |
| 200 | fertilisers | unreacted | Haber Process | recycled | pressure |

_____ is manufactured by the _____ _____. One use for ammonia is in the making of _____. The gases _____ and _____ are brought together under the special conditions of _____ °C and a _____ of _____ atmospheres. Nothing is wasted — any _____ hydrogen and nitrogen is _____. Hydrogen and nitrogen combine in a ratio of 3 _____ of _____ to 1 _____ of _____.

H Q6   In the production of ammonia, the yield increases as the pressure is increased. However, at a given pressure — the lower the temperature, the greater the yield.

    a) Using the data given in the table opposite, plot a **graph** of the variation of yield with pressure when the temperature is kept at 450°C.

    b) On the graph, **sketch a second line** showing the yields of ammonia you would expect at 350°C.

    c) Why is a **lower temperature** not used in ammonia production?

Pressure of reaction at 450°C (atm)	Approx. yield of ammonia (% volume)
100	10
200	25
300	40
400	45

Ammonia and Fertilisers

Q7 The reaction that produces ammonia is as follows:

Nitrogen + Hydrogen $\rightleftharpoons$ Ammonia

$$N_2 + 3H_2 \rightleftharpoons 2NH_3$$

a) This reaction is **exothermic**. What does this mean?

b) If you **increase the pressure**, what will happen to the yield of ammonia?

c) If the temperature is raised, the yield of ammonia is decreased, but the rate of reaction is much higher. **Why is this?**

d) The temperature in this industrial process is chosen to be high, although the yield is lower than it could be at a lower temperature. **Explain** why such a high temperature is chosen.

e) A high pressure will give an increased yield and an increase in the rate of reaction. **Explain** this statement in terms of particles, gases and the collision theory.

f) Iron is the catalyst used in this reaction. Why is it so **important** to have a catalyst?

Q8 Ammonia is made into fertilisers in three main stages.
Firstly, the ammonia needs to be converted into nitric acid.

Step 1 $$NH_{3(g)} + 5O_{2(g)} \xrightarrow{Pt} 4NO_{(g)} + H_2O_{(l)}$$

a) **Balance** this equation and state the **products** made in the reaction.

b) Ammonia reacts with oxygen as shown in this equation above. What conditions are needed?

Step 2 $$NO_{(g)} + 3O_{2\ (g)} + H_2O_{(g)} \rightarrow HNO_{3(aq)}$$

c) **Balance** the equation.

d) Name the **product** formed in this reaction.

Step 3 Nitric acid then needs to be converted into ammonium nitrate.

e) What **type** of reaction is this?

f) **Write** a word equation and a balanced symbol equation for this reaction.

g) Ammonium nitrate is a fertiliser. Which **element** in ammonium nitrate is particularly useful for plants?

h) What do plants **use** this element for?

Top Tips: You need to know the factors that improve the **rate of reaction** and the **yield**. Don't forget, yield and rate of reaction are favoured by different factors, so the **industrial conditions** are a **compromise**. The equations on this page are rather **boring**, but you do need to know them.

Limestone

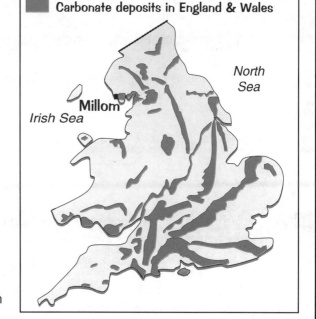

Carbonate deposits in England & Wales

North Sea

Millom

Irish Sea

Answer these questions about limestone's formation and uses

Q1 What is the main substance in **limestone**?

Q2 What **type of rock** is it?

Q3 **Name two** other rocks similar in chemical composition to limestone.

Q4 **Name three** areas shown on the map where there are carbonate deposits.

Q5 **How** has limestone formed?

Q6 Why is limestone used as a **building material**?

Q7 Why is limestone used as **road stone**?

Q8 When limestone is heated with sand and sodium carbonate it makes which **important material**?

Q9 What new material is formed when limestone is heated with **clay**?

Q10 The material in Q9 can be mixed with gravel. Give the **name** of this mixture and a **use** for it.

Q11 Mortar is a mixture of calcium hydroxide, sand and water. When the water dries out, the calcium hydroxide reacts with carbon dioxide to make calcium carbonate.
What **use** does it have?

Q12 Finely ground limestone is used to neutralise acidic soil. How does it **neutralise** the soil?

Q13 Why do farmers and gardeners often want to **neutralise** soils?

Q14 Calcium hydroxide forms when water is added to calcium oxide.

Give **another name** for calcium hydroxide.

Q15 Calcium hydroxide is also used to neutralise farm land.

What **kind of substance** is calcium hydroxide?

Q16 **Complete** the equation:

Sulphuric acid + Calcium carbonate → C_____ s_____ + W____ + C____ d_____
(from acid rain)

Q17 Why is the above reaction **damaging** to limestone buildings?

Q18 Limestone is used in the blast furnace, which is used to extract metals like iron.

What **job** does it do in this extraction process?

Top Tips: Limestone is mainly **calcium carbonate**. You've got to know how its made into **calcium oxide** and **calcium hydroxide** and what these are used **for**. Limestone is also used to make even more useful products like **cement** and **glass**.

Redox Reactions

Answer these questions on Redox Reactions:

H **Q1**   **Describe** reduction and oxidation in terms of the gain or loss of oxygen.

H **Q2**   **Describe** reduction and oxidation in terms of the gain or loss of hydrogen.

H **Q3**   **Describe** reduction and oxidation in terms of the gain or loss of electrons.

H **Q4**   **Copy** each of the equations below, adding
the names under the chemical formulae.

Please Note:
Due to printing restrictions, a "Red Ox"
could not be shown on this page.
Please be amused by this blue goat instead.

Then **mark with arrows** the oxidation and reduction
processes as shown below:

Reduction

$$CuO + C \rightarrow Cu + CO_2$$

Copper oxide + Carbon $\rightarrow$ Copper + Carbon dioxide

Oxidation

a) $CuO + H_2 \rightarrow Cu + H_2O$
b) $CuO + C \rightarrow Cu + CO$
c) $ZnO + CO \rightarrow Zn + CO_2$
d) $Fe_2O_3 + 3CO \rightarrow 2Fe + 3CO_2$
e) $MgO + 2Na \rightarrow Mg + Na_2O$

f) $ZnO + C \rightarrow Zn + CO$
g) $PbO_2 + 2CO \rightarrow Pb + 2CO_2$
h) $Pb_3O_4 + 4H_2 \rightarrow 4H_2O + 3Pb$
i) $Fe_3O_4 + 4CO \rightarrow 4CO_2 + 3Fe$
j) $CO_2 + C \rightarrow 2CO$

Top Tips: REDuction and OXidation reactions are just any reaction where one thing gives electrons to another. You can't really have one without the other, but you **can** have equations that only show one — **ionic equations**.

Equations

Q1 Complete the following **word** equations:

a)	Iron	+	sulphur	→	
b)	Iron	+	oxygen	→	
c)	Magnesium	+	oxygen	→	
d)	Sulphur	+	oxygen	→	
e)	Hydrogen	+	oxygen	→	
f)	Magnesium	+	sulphur	→	
g)	Aluminium	+	chlorine	→	
h)	Hydrogen	+	iodine	→	
i)	Carbon	+	oxygen	→	
j)	Iron	+	bromine	→	
k)	Potassium	+	chlorine	→	
l)	Iron	+	sulphur	→	
m)	Lead	+	oxygen	→	
n)	Calcium	+	oxygen	→	

Q2 Write out the following symbol equations in **words** (they are **not balanced**).

a) $CaCO_3$ → CaO + CO_2

b) MgO + $HCl_{(aq)}$ → $MgCl_2$ + H_2O

c) SO_2 + O_2 → SO_3

d) Na_2CO_3 + $HNO_{3(aq)}$ → $NaNO_3$ + H_2O + CO_2

e) N_2 + H_2 → NH_3

Q3 Write out the **symbol** equations below the word equations:

a) Carbon + oxygen → carbon dioxide

b) Zinc + sulphuric acid → zinc sulphate + hydrogen

c) Copper + chlorine → copper chloride

d) Hydrogen + copper oxide → copper + water

e) Magnesium + sulphuric acid → magnesium sulphate + hydrogen

f) Magnesium + copper sulphate → copper + magnesium sulphate

g) Copper carbonate → copper oxide + carbon dioxide

h) Potassium hydroxide + hydrochloric acid → potassium chloride + water

i) Sodium hydroxide + hydrochloric acid → sodium chloride + water

j) Calcium carbonate + sulphuric acid → calcium sulphate + water + carbon dioxide

Equations

Q4   Look at the following **equation:**

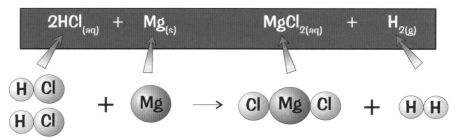

a) What do the terms (g), (aq) and (s) mean? What other similar symbol might be used?

b) What does the *2* before HCl mean?

c) Why is it $MgCl_2$ and not MgCl?

d) Why is it H_2 and not just H?

e) Write out the **symbol** equations below the picture equations, and **balance** them:

i)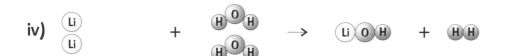

ii)

iii)

iv)

v)

Q5   **Write out** the equations below and **balance** them.

a) $CaCO_3$ $\rightarrow$ CaO + CO_2

b) MgO + HCl $\rightarrow$ $MgCl_2$ + H_2O

c) SO_2 + O_2 $\rightarrow$ SO_3

d) Na_2CO_3 + HNO_3 $\rightarrow$ $NaNO_3$ + H_2O + CO_2

e) N_2 + H_2 $\rightarrow$ NH_3

Top Tips:
Once you've checked each **element**, go back and check them all **again**. Keep doing this till **nothing** needs changing — then you'll know you've got it right. But whatever you do, don't change the numbers **inside** the formulae — that would completely change the reaction.

More Equations

Q1 **Balance** the following equations by putting the correct numbers before the formulae.

a) N_2 + H_2 → NH_3

b) $CaCO_3$ + H_2SO_4 → $CaSO_4$ + H_2O + CO_2

c) H_2 + O_2 → H_2O

d) Mg + O_2 → MgO

e) Ca + O_2 → CaO

f) H_2 + I_2 → HI

There's more...

g) Mg + H_2SO_4 → $MgSO_4$ + H_2

h) H_2SO_4 + $NaOH$ → Na_2SO_4 + H_2O

i) Ca + H_2SO_4 → $CaSO_4$ + H_2

j) H_2SO_4 + KOH → K_2SO_4 + H_2O

k) HCl + MgO → $MgCl_2$ + H_2O

l) CH_4 + O_2 → CO_2 + H_2O

m) H_2 + NO → H_2O + N_2

n) HCl + $Ca(OH)_2$ → $CaCl_2$ + H_2O

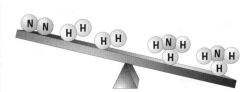

And more...

o) Fe_2O_3 + CO → Fe + CO_2

p) $C_6H_{12}O_6$ + O_2 → CO_2 + H_2O

q) CO_2 + H_2O → $C_6H_{12}O_6$ + O_2

r) C_4H_{10} + O_2 → CO_2 + H_2O

s) C_2H_4 + O_2 → CO_2 + H_2O

t) C_3H_8 + O_2 → CO_2 + H_2O

u) C_5H_{12} + O_2 → CO_2 + H_2O

v) C_3H_6 + O_2 → CO_2 + H_2O

w) C_2H_6 + O_2 → CO_2 + H_2O

Q2 **Tick** the following equations if they are balanced. If they are not balanced, **correct them**.

a) $4NH_{3(g)}$ + $5O_2$ → $NO_{(g)}$ + $H_2O_{(l)}$

b) $HCl_{(aq)}$ + $NaOH_{(aq)}$ → $NaCl_{(aq)}$ + $H_2O_{(aq)}$

c) $Na_{(s)}$ + $H_2O_{(l)}$ → $2NaOH_{(aq)}$ + $H_{2(g)}$

d) $KI_{(aq)}$ + $Cl_{2\ (g)}$ → $2KCl_{(aq)}$ + $I_{2(aq)}$

e) $Al_{(s)}$ + $Cl_{2(g)}$ → $2AlCl_{3\ (s)}$

f) $CaCO_{3(s)}$ + $HCl_{(aq)}$ → $CaCl_{2(aq)}$ + $H_2O_{(l)}$ + $CO_{2(g)}$

g) $ZnO_{(s)}$ + $C_{(s)}$ → $Zn_{(s)}$ + $CO_{2\ (g)}$

h) $CuCO_{3(s)}$ → $CuO_{(s)}$ + $CO_{2(g)}$

i) $CuO_{(s)}$ + $CH_{4(g)}$ → $Cu(s)$ + $CO_{2(g)}$ + $H_2O_{(l)}$

Relative Formula Mass

Sometimes you might be asked to: *"Find the Relative Formula Mass of ...."*;

other times you might be asked to: *"Find the mass of one mole of...."*

.....They're basically the same thing (but the second has grams after it).

Look at this example of an element question:

Example Question:

Find the relative atomic mass of zinc (which is basically the same as asking.... "Find the Mass of One Mole of Zinc")

Simply look on the periodic table (at the front of the book) for the relative atomic mass of zinc, which is 65, (add a "g" for grams if it asked for a mole) **<u>Answer</u> = <u>65</u>**

Find the relative atomic mass of...

Q1 calcium (Ca)

Q2 sodium (Na)

Q3 iron (Fe)

Q4 copper (Cu)

Q5 nitrogen (N)

Q6 carbon (**C**)

Q7 hydrogen (**H**)

Q8 chlorine (Cl)

Q9 potassium (K)

Q10 lithium (Li)

Q11 bromine

Q12 argon

Q13 titanium

Q14 aluminium

Q15 gold

Q16 silver

Q17 tungsten

Q18 caesium

Q19 mercury

Q20 lead

Look at this example of a molecule question:

Example Question:

Find the realtive formula mass of zinc oxide (which is basically the same as asking.... "Find the Mass of One Mole of Zinc oxide")

Simply look on the Periodic Table (at the front of the book) for the relative atomic masses of zinc and oxygen (65 and 16), add them up. (Then put a "g" for grams if it asked for a mole)

Zinc oxide has a formula ZnO. Which contains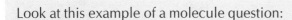

$$= (1 \times Zn) + (1 \times O)$$
$$= (1 \times 65) + (1 \times 16)$$
$$= \quad 65 \quad + \quad 16$$
$$= \quad \underline{81}$$

Find the Relative Formula Mass of ...

Q21 hydrogen molecules (H_2)

Q22 oxygen molecules (O_2)

Q23 chlorine molecules (Cl_2)

Q24 iodine molecules (I_2)

Q25 bromine molecules (Br_2)

Q26 nitrogen molecules (N_2)

Q27 fluorine molecules (F_2)

Q28 astatine (At_2)

Relative Formula Mass

Calculate the relative formula mass of the following compounds.

Q1 copper oxide (CuO)

Q2 magnesium oxide (MgO)

Q3 potassium iodide (KI)

Q4 potassium chloride (KCl)

Q5 hydrogen chloride (HCl)

Q6 sodium chloride (NaCl)

Q7 potassium bromide (KBr)

Q8 carbon monoxide (CO)

Q9 sodium bromide (NaBr)

Q10 lithium iodide (LiI)

Calculate the relative formula mass of these more complex compounds.

Q11 copper sulphate ($CuSO_4$)

Q12 carbon dioxide (CO_2)

Q13 water (H_2O)

Q14 methane (CH_4)

Q15 ammonia (NH_3)

Q16 calcium chloride ($CaCl_2$)

Q17 ethene (C_2H_4)

Q18 magnesium chloride ($MgCl_2$)

Q19 aluminium chloride ($AlCl_3$)

Q20 aluminium iodide (AlI_3)

Q21 sulphur dioxide (SO_2)

Q22 copper carbonate ($CuCO_3$)

Q23 zinc chloride ($ZnCl_2$)

Q24 ethane (C_2H_6)

Q25 barium sulphate ($BaSO_4$)

Q26 nitric acid (HNO_3)

Q27 lead iodide (PbI_2)

Q28 sulphuric acid (H_2SO_4)

Q29 aluminium oxide (Al_2O_3)

Q30 potassium nitrate (KNO_3)

And finally these hideously complex compounds.

Q31 calcium carbonate ($CaCO_3$)

Q32 sodium carbonate (Na_2CO_3)

Q33 aluminium hydroxide ($Al(OH)_3$)

Q34 glucose ($C_6H_{12}O_6$)

Q35 potassium manganate (VII) ($KMnO_4$)

Q36 sodium sulphate (Na_2SO_4)

Q37 tetrachloromethane (CCl_4)

Q38 citric acid ($C_6H_8O_7$)

Q39 ethanoic acid ($C_2H_4O_2$)

Q40 sodium hydrogen sulphate ($NaHSO_4$)

Q41 ammonium hydroxide (NH_4OH)

Q42 ammonium nitrate (NH_4NO_3)

Q43 ammonium sulphate (($NH_4)_2SO_4$)

Q44 ammonium phosphate (($NH_4)_3PO_4$)

Q45 calcium hydroxide ($Ca(OH)_2$)

Q46 aluminium sulphate ($Al_2(SO_4)_3$)

Q47 copper nitrate ($Cu(NO_3)_2$)

Q48 lead nitrate ($Pb(NO_3)_2$)

Q49 calcium nitrate ($Ca(NO_3)_2$)

Q50 potassium dichromate ($K_2Cr_3O_7$)

Top Tips: The trickiest thing is all the different terms — **molar mass**, **relative formula mass**, **mass of one mole**. But you work them out the same way — just remember that if something's **relative** it's being compared to something else, so it's **just a number** (a ratio) — it doesn't need grams after it.

% Element in a Compound

Remember this formula:

$$\text{\% Mass of an element in a compound} = \frac{A_r \times \text{No. of atoms (of that element)}}{M_r \text{ (of whole compound)}} \times 100$$

Here is an example worked out for you:

Find the % sodium in Na_2SO_4

$$\% \text{ Na} = \frac{A_r \times n}{M_r} \times 100 = \frac{23 \times 2}{142} \times 100 = \underline{32.4\%}$$

(Remember A_r = Relative Atomic Mass; M_r = Relative Molecular Mass)

Use the periodic table at the front of the book to answer the following:

For these simple compounds, find:

Q1 the % carbon in CO_2

Q2 the % carbon in CO

Q3 the % potassium in KCl

Q4 the % sodium in NaF

Q5 the % copper in CuO

Q6 the % sulphur in SO_2

Q7 the % oxygen in SO_2

Q8 the % sulphur in SO_3

Q9 the % oxygen in SO_3

Q10 the % hydrogen in H_2O

For these simple compounds, find:

Q11 the % nitrogen in NH_3

Q12 the % sodium in $NaOH$

Q13 the % water in $CuSO_4.5H_2O$

Q14 the % aluminium in Al_2O_3

Q15 the % copper in $CuCO_3$

Q16 the % copper in $CuSO_4$

Q17 the % potassium in KNO_3

Q18 the % phosphorus in $(NH_4)_3PO_4$

Q19 the % nitrogen in NH_4NO_3

Q20 the % nitrogen in $(NH_4)_2SO_4$

Q21 Which has the greater proportion of carbon? **a)** CH_4 **b)** C_6H_6 **c)** C_2H_5OH
Show how you calculated your answer.

Q22 Which has the greater proportion of aluminium? **a)** Al_2O_3 **b)** Na_3AlF_6

Q23 Which of these iron ores has the most iron in it by percentage mass?
a) siderite ($FeCO_3$) **b)** haematite (Fe_2O_3) **c)** magnetite (Fe_3O_4) **d)** iron pyrite (FeS_2)

Q24 Calculate the proportion of metal in: **a)** $NaCl$ **b)** $MgCO_3$ **c)** Zn **d)** KOH

Q25 The molar mass of haemoglobin is about 33939g.
If each molecule contains two iron atoms, what percentage of the molecule is iron?

Top Tips: This might seem a bit tricky, but it's basically the **same technique** each time — once you've got it, you'll sail through them. Learn some common **atomic masses** to speed things up — and use the extra time to **check your answers** — it's so easy to make mistakes.

Empirical Formulae

H   To find out the empirical formula for a compound you must find the amount of each element and
then calculate the simplest whole number ratio of the amounts. Look at the example below.

A compound is 75% carbon and 25% hydrogen. What is its empirical formula?

Assume sample weighs 100g 👉

This'll turn it into an easy ratio for the formula. 👉

Elements	Carbon	Hydrogen
% Element =	75	= 25
Mass (g) =	75	= 25
Divide by A_r for each element =	$\frac{75}{12} = 6.25$	$= \frac{25}{1} = 25$
$\dfrac{\text{Amount}}{\text{Smallest amount}} =$	$\dfrac{6.25}{6.25}$	$= \dfrac{25}{6.25}$
Ratio of amount =	1	: 4

C_1H_4 or, better, $\boxed{CH_4}$

Answer these two-element questions:

H Q1   A hydrocarbon is 80% carbon and 20% hydrogen. Find its **empirical formula**.

H Q2   A compound was found to have 82% nitrogen and 18% hydrogen. Find its **empirical formula**.

H Q3   An oxide of carbon was found to be 27% carbon. Find its **empirical formula**.

H Q4   An oxide of sulphur was found to be 40% sulphur. Find its **empirical formula**.

H Q5   Fluorspar is composed of calcium and fluorine. If 51% is calcium, **calculate** the empirical formula.

H Q6   Magnetite is an oxide ore of iron. If 72% is iron, what is its **empirical formula**?

And these three-element questions:

H Q7   Cryolite is an ore of aluminium used in the extraction of aluminium from bauxite;

it was found to have 33% sodium, 13% aluminium and 54% fluorine.

Work out the empirical formula.

H Q8   Nitram is an ammonium fertiliser; it is 35% nitrogen, 5% hydrogen and 60% oxygen.

Calculate its empirical formula.

H Q9   Saltpetre is a potassium salt; it is 13.9% nitrogen, 38.6% potassium and 47.5% oxygen.

Work out its empirical formula.

H Q10   Caustic soda is a strong alkali containing sodium.

It is 40.0% oxygen, 57.5% sodium and 2.5% hydrogen.

Calculate its empirical formula.

Empirical Formulae

H

The method used on Page 41 uses the % of an element in a compound — but the same method can be used if the mass of an element is given. Here's an example:

Calculate the empirical formula of a compound made by combining 1.92g of magnesium with 5.68g of chlorine.

	Magnesium	Chlorine
Mass (g)	= 1.92	= 5.68
Molar mass (g)	= 24	= 35.5
Divide by A_r for each element	$= \dfrac{1.92}{24} = 0.08$	$= \dfrac{5.68}{35.5} = 0.16$
$\dfrac{\text{Amount}}{\text{Smallest amount}}$	$= \dfrac{0.08}{0.08} = 1$	$= \dfrac{0.16}{0.08} = 2$
Ratio of amounts	= 1	: 2

Mg_1Cl_2 or, better, $\boxed{MgCl_2}$

Use the example to help you answer these two-element questions:

Q11 2.70g of aluminium is combined with 10.65g of chlorine.
What is the **empirical formula** of the new compound?

Q12 1.68g of iron is combined with 0.48g of oxygen.
What is the **empirical formula** of the new compound?

Q13 1.6g of sulphur was heated in oxygen. Its mass increased to 4.0g. What is the **name** of this oxide of sulphur? Show how you found this out by **calculating** its empirical formula.

Q14 190.5g of copper reacts with 48g of oxygen. **Calculate** the empirical formula.

Q15 A sample of lead chloride was found to contain 82.8g of lead and 28.4g of chlorine.
What is its **empirical formula**?

Q16 0.48g of magnesium is heated strongly in a crucible until it had completely reacted with the oxygen in the air. The mass of the new compound was found to be 0.80g.

a) **Name** the new compound.

b) Calculate the **mass** of oxygen that has been added to the magnesium.

c) Calculate the **empirical formula**.

Use the example to help you answer these two-element questions:

Q17 1.48g of a calcium compound contains 0.8g of calcium, 0.64g of oxygen and 0.04g of hydrogen. **Calculate** the empirical formula and name the compound.

Q18 Copper sulphate crystals contain **water of crystallisation** *(water in its crystal structure)* and have the formula $CuSO_4.xH_2O$, where x is a number. 49.9g of a sample of copper sulphate was found to have 18g of water of crystallisation. **Calculate** x.

Top Tips: Empirical formulae are **not** the same thing as real (**molecular**) formulae — you've got to **cancel** those numbers. So, ethene's molecular formula is C_2H_4, but its empirical formula is CH_2 — you're writing the **ratio** of the numbers of **moles** in its **simplest form**.

Reacting Amount Calculations

Use the equations given to answer these questions:

H Q1 **Work out** the mass of **iron sulphide** produced when 5.6g of iron completely reacts with excess sulphur.

$$Fe \; + \; S \; \rightarrow \; FeS$$

H Q2 **Calculate** the mass of **iron sulphide** produced when 320g of sulphur is reacted with excess iron.

H Q3 **Calculate** the mass of iron required to make 8.8g of **iron sulphide** by reacting iron with sulphur.

H Q4 What is the mass of **magnesium oxide** produced when 48g of magnesium is oxidised in **air** to make magnesium oxide.

$$2Mg \; + \; O_2 \; \rightarrow \; 2MgO$$

H Q5 **Calculate** the mass of carbon dioxide that is released when 20g of calcium carbonate **decomposes** on heating.

Calcium carbonate

$$CaCO_3 \; \rightarrow \; CaO \; + \; CO_2$$

H Q6 What is the mass of calcium carbonate needed to make 560g of **calcium oxide**?

H Q7 Copper carbonate **decomposes** on heating to form copper oxide. What mass of copper carbonate is needed to make 8g of copper oxide?

Copper carbonate

H Q8 How much carbon would be needed to make 8.8g of carbon dioxide?

$$C \; + \; O_2 \; \rightarrow \; CO_2$$

Answer these industrial questions:

H Q9 What **mass** of iron would be obtained from 160 tonnes of iron(III) oxide?

$$Fe_2O_3 \; + \; 3CO \; \rightarrow \; 2Fe \; + \; 3CO_2$$

H Q10 Ammonia is manufactured by the Haber Process, which involves the following reaction between nitrogen and hydrogen:

H₂
N₂

$$N_2 \; + \; 3H_2 \rightarrow \; 2NH_3$$

NH₃

What mass of **a)** nitrogen,
b) hydrogen

......would be required to make 340g of ammonia?

Reacting Amount Calculations

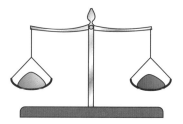

H Q11 Which has the **greater number** of atoms:

230g of sodium or 230g of potassium?

H Q12 Which has the **least number** of atoms:

5g of hydrogen gas or 10g of helium?

H Q13 What mass of nitrogen gas has the same number of **particles** as 320g of oxygen gas?

H Q14 How much **anhydrous** $CuSO_4$ is produced when 22.4g of

hydrated copper sulphate $(CuSO_4.5H_2O)$ is gently heated?

H Q15 How much aluminium oxide would be needed to make the following **amounts** of aluminium?

a) 1kg   **b)** 2kg   **c)** 4.5kg   **d)** 1 tonne *(1 tonne = 1000kg)*

$$2Al_2O_3 \rightarrow 4Al + 3O_2$$

H Q16 Copper oxide can be **reduced** to copper using methane.

How much copper oxide would be needed to make 19.2g of copper?

$$4CuO + CH_4 \rightarrow 4Cu + CO_2 + 2H_2O$$

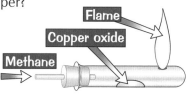

H Q17 How much calcium oxide is produced by heating 25 tonnes of calcium carbonate?

$$CaCO_3 \rightarrow CaO + CO_2$$

H Q18 What mass of water is produced by completely **burning** 15kg of butane?

$$2C_4H_{10} + 13O_2 \rightarrow 8CO_2 + 10H_2O$$

Top Tips: These are just **jazzed-up mole calculations** — but they're typical Exam questions.
You've got to look at an **entire equation** instead of just one formula — but the method's basically the **same**. In practice you'd never get as much product as you calculate here — there'll always be a bit left unreacted, or some gas escaping. In other words, you'll have **less than 100% yield**.

Calculating Volumes

To answer these questions you must know that a mass of M_r in grams, of any gas, will always occupy 24 litres (that's 24,000 cm³) at room temperature and pressure (RTP)

RTP is...
25°C
1 atmosphere pressure.

If you are asked to convert a mass of gas to a volume of gas, first you need to be able to convert the mass to moles — or simply remember this equation:

$$\frac{\text{Volume of gas (in cm}^3)}{24,000} = \frac{\text{Mass of gas}}{M_r \text{ of gas}}$$

Look at this example:
What is the volume of 0.2g of H_2?

$$\frac{\text{Vol. of gas}}{24,000} = \frac{0.2}{2} \qquad \text{Vol. of gas} = \frac{0.2 \times 24,000}{2} = 2,400 \text{cm}^3$$

H Q1 Find the **volume at RTP** of the following:

a) 8g of helium (He) in litres

b) 4g of argon (Ar) in litres

c) 8.4g of krypton (Kr) in litres

d) 2.6g of xenon (Xe) in cm³

e) 32g of oxygen (O_2) in cm³

f) 7.1g of chlorine (Cl_2) in cm³

H Q2 Find the **volume at RTP** of the following:

a) 11g of CO_2 in litres

b) 40g of CH_4 in litres

c) 8g of SO_3 in cm³

d) 25.5g of NH_3 in cm³

e) 131.75g of CH_3NH_2 in cm³ *(don't know if that's a gas at RTP, but I liked the look of it)*

Calculating Volumes

If the question gives you the volume and asks you for the mass, you can get it from the equation at the top of the last page. Practise on these ones.

H Q3   Find the **mass** of the following volumes of gas (they're at RTP):

a) 24 litres of He

b) 3 litres of He

c) 18 litres O_2

d) 2000 cm³ of O_3

e) 3000 cm³ of H_2

H Q4   Find the **mass** of the following volumes of gas (they're at RTP):

a) 24 litres of C_2H_4

b) 30 litres of NH_3

c) 6200 cm³ SO_2

d) 9600 cm³ of CH_3NH_2 *(still don't know if that's a gas at RTP, but still like the look of it)*

H Q5   **Consider** the equation:

$$Mg \; + \; H_2SO_4 \; \rightarrow \; MgSO_4 \; + \; H_2$$

a) Calculate the mass of hydrogen produced when 2.4g of magnesium reacts completely with the acid.

b) Calculate the volume of hydrogen produced at RTP in part **a)**.

c) Calculate the mass of magnesium required to produce 4g of hydrogen.

d) Calculate the volume of 4g of hydrogen.

e) Calculate the mass of magnesium required to produce 1,200cm³ of hydrogen.

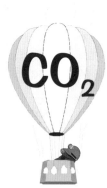

Top Tips:

Volume doesn't depend on **type of gas**. Temperature and pressure affect it, but they'll be constant in Exam questions — probably **RTP** (make sure you can define this). Don't think you can forget tricky stuff like this, **5%** of the Exam could be on it — pretty much a **grade**... so keep **practising**, until you get them **ALL** right each time.

Electrolysis

H Q1   Answer these questions on electrolysis:

a) What is the correct name for the **positive** electrode?

b) What is the correct name for the **negative** electrode?

c) What do these **terms** mean?

     Cl^- Na^+ $NaCl_{(s)}$ $Cl_{2(g)}$

H Q2   The diagram shows electrolysis in action.

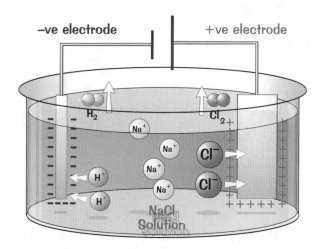

–ve electrode   +ve electrode

H_2 Cl_2

Na^+ Na^+ Cl^- H^+ Na^+ Cl^- H^+

NaCl Solution

a) **How many** electrons would be needed to neutralise one sodium ion (Na^+)?

b) **How many** electrons would be needed to neutralise one mole of sodium ions (Na^+)?

     (1 mole = 6.02×10^{23})

c) What is the **mass** of one mole of sodium? *(I.e. what is its Relative Formula Mass?)*

H Q3   Answer the questions below:

a) **Complete** the sentence:

> If one mole of _____ is supplied to one mole
>
> of sodium _____, they are neutralised to
>
> produce _____ g of sodium atoms.

$$2Cl^- \rightarrow Cl_2 + 2e^-$$

b) Two electrons and one molecule of chlorine are produced from two chlorine ions:

    i) How many moles of chlorine gas would be made if two moles of chloride ions were neutralised?

    ii) What volume in cm^3 would this number of moles of chlorine occupy at RTP?

Acid Rain

Rainwater is naturally acidic due to carbon dioxide in the atmosphere. This dissolves in water to make a weakly acidic solution.

Carbon dioxide + Water → Carbonic acid

However combustion of fossil fuel releases pollutants into the atmosphere like sulphur dioxide and oxides of nitrogen. These also react with water and produce an even more acidic solution.

Sulphur dioxide + Water → Sulphurous acid
(Further oxidation produces sulphuric acid)

At very high temperatures inside a car engine, nitrogen oxidises to make oxides of nitrogen, often written as NO_x (because many oxides form). These can form nitric acid on reaction with water. The acid rain falls down to Earth, damaging the environment.

Q1   Why is rain water **naturally acidic**? *Which acid does it naturally contain?*

Q2   **Write out** a symbol equation for the reaction of carbon dioxide with water.

Q3   What is a **fossil fuel**?

Q4   **Name** three fossil fuels.

Q5   Give another **name** for combustion.

Q6   Name **three** pollutant gases which are released on combustion of some fossil fuels?

Q7   **Name two** acids which are not naturally found in rain water.

Q8   What effect do you think acid rain might have on **a)** fish in lakes **b)** trees in forests?

Q9   *Most of the sulphur dioxide produced worldwide comes from industry and power stations.*

   a) What do power stations **burn** to produce sulphur dioxide?

   b) What do you feel they should do to **reduce the level** of this gas in the atmosphere?

Q10   *Power stations now have chemical scrubbers that remove the acid gases in the emissions.* **Give the name** of a type of reaction that will remove the acid gases.

Q11   Name a **cheap substance** that could be used to remove these gases.

Q12   *Road traffic is a major producer of oxides of nitrogen.*

   a) What other very **harmful gas** is found in significant quantities in exhaust fumes?

   b) *Nickel and rhodium can be used to reduce exhaust emission from cars by converting the carbon monoxide to carbon dioxide and the oxides of nitrogen to nitrogen.*
   Give the **advantages** and **disadvantages** of this.

Top Tips:
These things really bring home how delicate the atmosphere is. There's three parts here — the **greenhouse effect**, **acid rain**, and the **ozone hole** — and being pretty topical, they're likely to be in the Exam. They're all completely **separate** — make sure you understand why. Try drawing a **flow diagram** for each effect — that'll tell you if you really know them. Make sure you know the **causes** and **effects** for each.

The Greenhouse Effect

Most scientists think that the Greenhouse Effect will contribute to global warming. This happens because greenhouse gases, like carbon dioxide and methane, trap infrared radiation inside the atmosphere, which causes it to warm. The higher temperatures could cause the ice caps to melt — raising the sea levels. With more water about, low-lying areas could flood, while other areas of the world could experience severe droughts.

Q1 Explain using the diagram opposite how a greenhouse keeps plants warm.

Q2 How is the **radiant energy** in sunlight kept in the greenhouse?

Q3 Explain using the diagram opposite how the atmosphere can act like a **greenhouse**, warming the planet up (the atmosphere is **not** drawn to scale).

Q4 What might happen to **global temperatures** if the greenhouse effect continues to intensify?

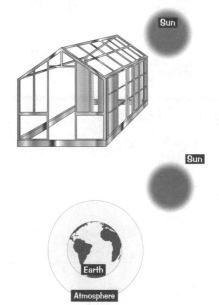

Q5 The table opposite lists the main contributors to the greenhouse effect.

a) **Draw** a pie chart to illustrate these results.

b) Which gas is the **main contributor** to this effect?

c) What are humans doing to **increase** the levels of this gas in the atmosphere?

Gas	% Greenhouse Gas
Methane	14
CFCs	14
Nitrogen	5
Carbon dioxide	57
Surface ozone	10

Q6 Look at the table opposite.

a) What happened in the **early 1800s** to account for the rise in global temperatures?

b) Figures are projected for the years 2050 and 2100. What can **we do** to ensure these figures are not reached?

Year	Approximate global temperature change
1800	0.0
1850	0.1
1900	0.2
1950	0.5
2000	1.0
2050	2.0
2100	4.0

The Atmosphere

Q1   *Copper turnings were placed in a tube connected to two gas syringes as shown in the diagram below. The air in the syringes was passed backwards and forwards over the copper as it was heated. After heating for five minutes the apparatus was allowed to cool and the volume of air left in the syringe was noted.*

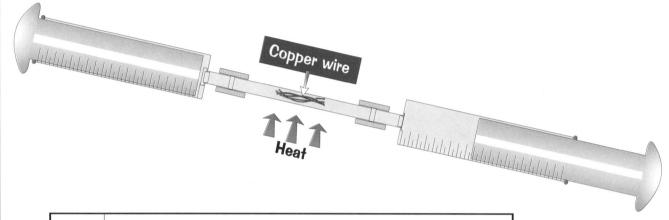

Results.

	Volume of Air	Copper	
Start	200cm^3	orange	
Finish	158cm^3	black	

a) From the results, **calculate** the reduction in volume of air.

b) **Work this out** as a percentage of air.

c) What is the name of the **active component** of air which has apparently disappeared?

d) **Where** do you think the gas has gone?

e) **Construct** a word equation to show exactly what has happened to the copper.

f) Why do you think the apparatus was **allowed to cool** before a final reading was taken?

g) Name a gas **still present** in the syringes at the end of the experiment and give a **use** for this gas.

'arry just couldn't get over 'is 'at moss fear.

The Atmosphere

The graphs below give information about the Earth's atmosphere millions of years ago and today.

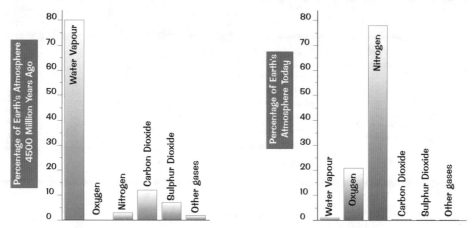

Q2   Could the early atmosphere **support life** as we know it? Explain your answer.

Q3   *About 3,000 million years ago simple organisms started to photosynthesise. Which gas did this remove from the early atmosphere?* **Write** a word and symbol equation for this reaction.

Q4   Which organisms caused the increase in oxygen and the decrease in carbon dioxide?

Q5   What role did the ocean play in the reduction of carbon dioxide?

Q6   What might have been responsible for the decrease in water vapour?

Q7   Gases like methane and ammonia were found in the Earth's early atmosphere. Look at the equations below and use them to **explain** the changes in the composition of the Earth's atmosphere.

> Ammonia + Oxygen $\rightarrow$ Nitrogen + Water
> $$4NH_{3\,(g)} + 3O_{2(g)} \rightarrow 2N_{2(g)} + 6H_2O_{(g)}$$
> Methane + Oxygen $\rightarrow$ Carbon dioxide + Water
> $$CH_{4(g)} + 2O_{2(g)} \rightarrow CO_{2(g)} + 2H_2O_{(g)}$$

Q8   *Bacteria convert ammonia into nitrates. How does this help plant growth?*

Q9   *About 350 million years ago animals started to develop. Animals do not require sunlight to make food.* **Which gas** did they require to be present to survive?

Q10   *Animals respire.* Write a **word equation** for respiration.

Q11   *Carbon that has been locked up for millions of years is returned to the atmosphere when fossil fuels are burnt.* **Write** an equation for this reaction.

Q12   *The sea and plants remove carbon dioxide from the atmosphere.*
          What will happen if processes that absorb the **additional** carbon dioxide released into the atmosphere from combustion of fossil fuels are **removed**?

Top Tips:
This basically boils down to knowing your atmosphere, and knowing how its composition's affected by things like **respiration**, **photosynthesis** and **burning**. Make sure you know at least rough percentages for **nitrogen**, **oxygen**, **argon** and **carbon dioxide** (these are always for **dry** air, as the **water vapour's** pretty variable). And don't forget that if something's being burnt or oxidised, gases might be **released** — so always think of the **equation**.

The Rock Cycle

Q1   *Look at the diagram of the rock cycle opposite.*

a) **Fill in** the boxes with words from the list below:

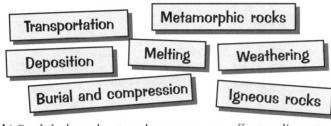

Transportation   Metamorphic rocks   Deposition   Melting   Weathering   Burial and compression   Igneous rocks

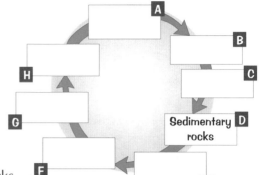

A B C H G Sedimentary rocks D F E

b) **Explain** how heat and pressure can affect sedimentary rocks.

c) *"Metamorphic rocks form by recrystallisation"*. What is meant by this?

d) **Give two** examples of ways rocks can be weathered.

Q2   *The diagram opposite shows part of the rock cycle.*

a) **Label** parts (i) to (iv).

b) **Explain the difference** between magma and lava.

c) What will happen to the rock in the shaded area (v)?

d) What type of rock would you find at (v) and why?

e) What will eventually happen to the rock at (vi)?

f) **Explain the difference** between the rock formed at (i) and at (iv) on the diagram.

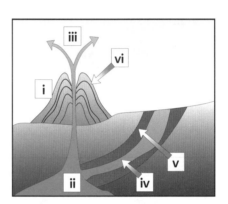

Q3   **Fill in** the table below to explain the following words and how they relate to the rock cycle.

Description	Meaning	Associated with forming:
a) Deposition		Sedimentary rock
b) Burial		Sedimentary and metamorphic rock
c) Melting		
d) Compression		
e) Recrystallisation		

Q4   **Complete** the following paragraphs by filling in the missing words from the list:

buried   igneous   metamorphic   weathered   buried   compressed   heat
melted   magma   sedimentary   millions   sedimentary   metamorphic   magma
sea   pressure   magma   volcano   erupts   rock cycle

Over _____ of years rocks change from one form to another. This is called the
_____. The three main rock types are _____, _____ and
igneous. Rock particles get washed into the _____ because they are _____
and transported. Over millions of years these become _____ and
_____, and form _____ rock. Sometimes these rocks become
_____ deeper into the Earth, and are changed by _____ and
_____ into _____ rocks. Metamorphic rock can be buried still further
where, completely _____, it becomes _____. Pressure forces the
_____ upwards where it either _____ as a _____ or goes into
existing cracks in rock and forms _____ rock.

The Rock Cycle

Q5 What does **metamorphic** mean?

Q6 What is the general **term** given to:

a) igneous rock that forms **outside** the crust (from volcanoes).

b) igneous rock that cools in cracks **in existing rock**.

Q7 **Fill in** the table by **naming** the metamorphic rocks formed from the sedimentary rocks.

Sedimentary rock	Metamorphic rock
a) Limestone	
b) Mudstone	
c) Sandstone	

Q8 *Sedimentary and metamorphic rocks are formed deep underground.*
Explain how it is possible to see these rocks on the Earth's **surface**.

Q9 Considering how each type of rock is formed, **explain** why igneous rock is more resistant to weathering than sedimentary rock.

Q10 **Give two differences** between metamorphic and igneous rocks.

Q11 What name is given to the particles that weather and settle in the sea?

Q12 *The diagram below shows an outline of the rock cycle.*

a) **Label** all the areas where you would expect to find:

i) metamorphic rocks.   ii) sedimentary rocks.   iii) igneous rocks.

b) Put the **following labels** onto the diagram:

- i) weathering
- ii) heat and pressure
- iii) melting
- iv) compression
- v) burial
- vi) recrystallisation
- vii) eruption
- viii) deposition
- ix) transport

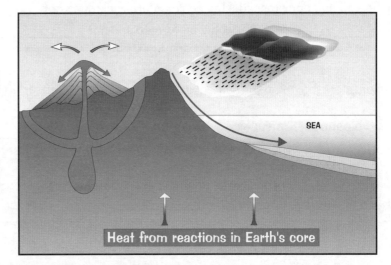

SEA

Heat from reactions in Earth's core

c) **Explain** in your own words how:

i) sedimentary rocks get changed into metamorphic rocks.

ii) metamorphic rocks get changed into igneous rocks.

iii) igneous and metamorphic rocks get changed into sedimentary rocks.

Top Tips:

Another cycle to learn. But since there's only **three** basic **rock types**, it really isn't so bad. Draw them in a **triangle**, then think how each can be converted into the other two — and fill in the arrows. There's only **six combinations**, so you'll know if you've missed anything. Just make sure you can **name** all the processes — and know the **conditions** they need.

A Summary of Rock Types

Q1   Match the correct rock to the type:

Marble   Sandstone

Shale   Schist

Slate   Granite

Igneous

Sedimentary

Metamorphic

Q2   Complete the following sentences using the correct words from the list below:

| metamorphic | crystallise | large | cement | fossils | melted | basalt |
| water | granite | pressure | cements | melt | sedimentary | magma |

_____ is an example of an intrusive igneous rock. It has _____ crystals. _____ is an example of an extrusive igneous rock. Sedimentary rocks contain _____ which will not be present in igneous or metamorphic rocks because they would have _____ or changed. Sedimentary rocks contain a natural _____ which is made because _____ squeezes the _____ out and salts _____, which _____ particles together. Metamorphic rocks are formed when _____ rocks are heated and compressed. The sedimentary rock does not _____ or _____ would be formed and not _____ rock.

Q3   Complete the following sentences using the correct words from the list below:

| volcano | intrusive | magma | small | large | extrusive | erupts |

a) _____ igneous rocks cool slowly and have _____ crystals. _____ goes into existing cracks in rock.

b) _____ igneous rocks cool quickly and have _____ crystals. Magma _____ from the inside of the earth in a _____.

Q4   Complete the following sentences using the correct words from the list below:

| heat | sedimentary | heated | melt | texture | injection | metamorphic | Earth | pressure |

_____ rocks are changed into _____ rock by _____ and _____. _____ movements push rocks underground. The _____ of metamorphic rocks is changed but the rocks do not _____. If they did, they would not be metamorphic rocks. Metamorphic rocks can also form when an _____ of magma in cracks in existing rocks causes the rock around to be _____.

Sedimentary Rocks

Q1   *The diagram shows the formation of sedimentary rocks.*

   a) Explain what happens when pressure is
   applied to a layer of sedimentary rock.

   b) How is the cement that holds pieces of
   sedimentary rock together formed?

   c) Why are fossils found in sedimentary
   rocks but not in igneous or
   metamorphic rock?

   d) Draw **arrows** on the diagram to show
   which way the following act:

   i) transport **ii)** pressure

   e) *Plant and animal remains decay in
   sedimentary rock to make a useful
   substance.*
   Name this useful substance.

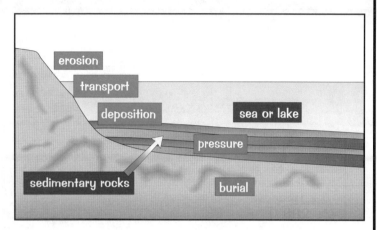

Q2   *Sedimentary rocks are fragments of other rocks in a natural cement.*
   Explain why the rocks that they are made from can still be identified.

Q3   **Match** the rocks with the correct descriptions below:

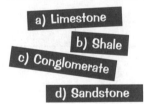

   a) Limestone

   b) Shale

   c) Conglomerate

   d) Sandstone

   i) Formed from fine particles grey in colour. Will easily split into layers.

   ii) Pebbles and chips of rock in a cement.

   iii) Made from sand. Particles stuck together.

   iv) Formed from shells, mostly calcium carbonate, grey/white colour.

Q4   **Explain** how fossils found in sedimentary rock are used to date the rocks.

Q5   *Look at the diagram below.*

   a) i) In which layer(s) could **limestone** be found?

   ii) In which layer(s) could **marble** be found?

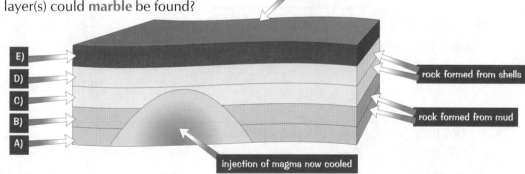

   b) Which layers would you find the **least fossils** in?

   c) Which layer is: **i)** the **oldest** rock, **ii)** the **youngest** rock?

   d) *Some of these rock layers are sedimentary.*
   Explain what this tells us about the **formation** of this land.

   e) What **type of rock** would the **magma** have formed?

Sedimentary Rocks

Q6   *Earth movements cause layers of sedimentary rock to move.*
An example is shown in the diagram below:

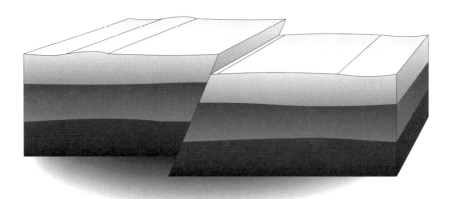

   a) How can you tell that the Earth's crust has **moved?**

   b) What is this formation **called?**

   c) *Although it can be seen that these rocks have moved, it is*
   dating the sedimentary rocks that tells us they are the same age.

   Explain how sedimentary rocks can be dated.

Q7   *Look at the diagrams below of different rock fragments.*

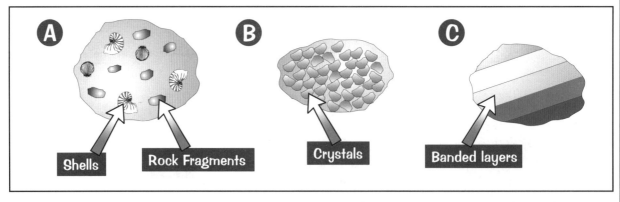

   a) For each of A, B and C, state whether it is an igneous, a sedimentary or a metamorphic rock.
   Give a reason for your choice in each case.

   b) **Name** a possible example of each type of rock.

Q8   *Granite is much harder than limestone.* **Explain why**.

Top Tips:

Pretty straightforward really, these sedimentary rocks — just loads of **particles** stuck in a **cement**.
But you'd better know **what** the cement is — and **where** it comes from. The Exams might ask you
to identify a sedimentary rock from a picture, so you'd better know a few. Make sure you at least
know the differences between **sandstone**, **limestone**, **mudstone** (**shale**) and **conglomerates**.

Metamorphic Rocks

Q1   What causes rocks underground to be subjected to large forces?

Q2   *The diagram below shows a section of the rock cycle where metamorphic rocks form.*

a) **Write** on the diagram:

i) where **pressure** acts.

ii) where **heat** comes from.

b) Why do metamorphic rocks **recrystallise**?

c) Where in the diagram might **magma** be formed?

d) Where does the **heat** come from to cause rock changes?

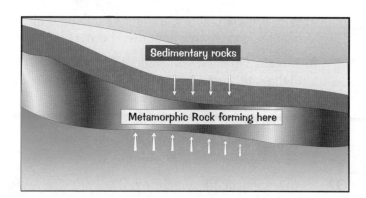

Q3   **Identify** the following metamorphic rocks from their descriptions:

a) | Small sugary crystals, white/grey in colour |

b) | Grey, can be split into layers |

c) | Layers of crystals, including dark mica |

Q4   *Slate and schist are both formed from mudstone and shale.*

What causes the **difference** between them?

Q5   *People grow crops near volcanic areas even though there are risks of volcanic eruptions.*

Explain why the soil there is **so fertile**.

Q6   *Look at the table below.*

a) **Complete** the table by giving uses for the various types of rock.

Rock	Use
Sandstone	
Limestone	
Slate	
Marble	

b) Why are metamorphic rocks generally **harder** and more **resistant to erosion** than sedimentary rocks?

Top Tips:
Exam favourites include how **crystal sizes** of igneous rocks depend on the **rate of cooling**, and how particular metamorphic rocks have formed. You'd better know your **slate** from your **marble** and **schist** — and know **what** they're formed from, and under what **conditions**. And make sure you can tell **intrusive** from **extrusive** igneous rocks.

Igneous Rocks

Q1 *The size of an igneous rock's crystals depends on the rock's rate of cooling when it was being formed. It is possible to set up an experiment in the lab using SALOL to investigate the relationship between crystal size and rate of cooling. The apparatus is shown opposite. The salol melts to form a clear liquid, which can then be removed and recrystallised.*

a) Why is it better to use a water bath than to directly heat the crystals over a Bunsen burner?

b) Explain a method you could use to ensure that
  (i) the salol cooled quickly
  (ii) the salol cooled slowly

c) Which would give the larger crystals?

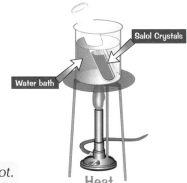

Q2 *In some igneous rocks the crystals are visible and in some they are not.*

  Explain the following: **a)** why some igneous rocks have **small crystals**

  b) why some igneous rocks have **large crystals**

Q3 **Label** the diagram on the right.

a) Indicate where you would find:

  i) Extrusive igneous rock.

  ii) Intrusive igneous rock.

  iii) Magma.

  iv) Lava.

b) Name one intrusive and one extrusive igneous rock.

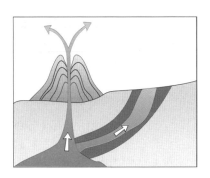

Q4 *The diagram below shows a piece of igneous rock amongst layers of sedimentary rock.*

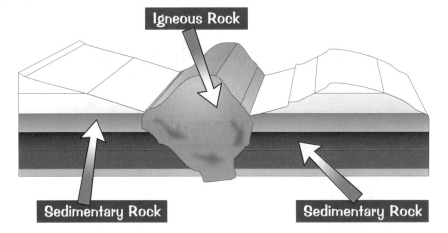

a) How do you think this igneous rock came to be here?

b) Explain why in a few thousand years this lump of igneous rock may stand well above the rest of the landscape.

Q5 Sometimes igneous rock, such as pumice, can be very light and have holes in it. **Explain** how pumice is formed and why it has this form.

The Periodic Table

Q1 In the Periodic table what is meant by a **Group**?

Q2 In the Periodic table what is meant by a **Period**?

Q3 Roughly **how many** elements are there?

Q4 In what **order** are the elements listed? 1 - 8

Q5 What might be **similar** about members of the same group?

Q6 What might be **similar** about members of the same period?

Q7 Whose **idea** was it to put the elements in this order?

Q8 If an element is in Group I then **how many** electrons will it have in its outer electron shell?

Q9 If an ion has a 2+ charge, then **which group** is it most likely to be in?

Q10 If an ion has a 1- charge, then **which group** is it most likely to be in?

Q11 In this Periodic Table, some elements are shown as letters:

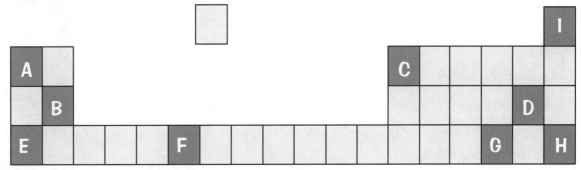

These letters are NOT the proper symbols for the elements.

Choose **one** letter from the above Periodic Table to answer each of the following questions:

WHICH ELEMENT(S).........

   (a) are Noble gases?

   (b) are Halogens?

   (c) is in Group II?

   (d) is in the same period as D?

   (e) has three electrons in its outer shell?

   (f) has an atomic number of 3?

   (g) are non-metals?

   (h) is a transition element?

   (i) would form an ION with a charge of 1^+?

   (j) will not form an ion easily?

   (k) would form an ion by gaining 2 electrons per atom?

   (l) would form an ion with as many electrons as an atom of element (I)?

   (m) are the least reactive of those marked in the table?

Q12 **Complete** this table by filling in the **electronic configurations** of the elements:

Period	Group 1		Group 2	Group 3	Group 7	Group 0	
2	Li	2,1	Be	B	F	Ne	
3	Na		Mg	Al	Cl	Ar	2,8,8

The Periodic Table

Q13   Select the correct *italicised* words to describe Group I:

a) All the elements are *metals* / *non-metals*.

b) They are all *hard* / *soft* substances with a *high* / *low* density.

c) They are all very *reactive* / *unreactive* and are kept in a bottle of *oil* / *water*.

d) They tarnish *easily* / *with difficulty* in air.

e) They become *more* / *less* reactive going down the Group.

f) A typical member of the group is *calcium* / *sodium*.

g) They form *1^+* / *1^-* ions.

Q14   Select the correct *italicised* words to describe Group VII:

a) All the elements are *metallic* / *non-metallic*.

b) They are mostly *conductors* / *non-conductors* of electricity.

c) Going down the Group their melting points *increase* / *decrease*.

d) Chlorine is a *solid* / *liquid* / *gas* at RTP.

e) Bromine is a *solid* / *liquid* / *gas* at RTP.

f) Iodine is a *solid* / *liquid* / *gas* at RTP.

g) Down the Group they get *lighter* / *darker* in colour.

h) They form *1^+* / *1^-* ions.

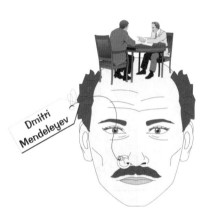

Dmitri Mendeleyev

Q15   Many Periodic Tables have a **zig-zag** line on them. What does this line **divide**?

Q16   **Where** are the **metals** in the Periodic Table in relation to this line?

Q17   **Where** are the **non-metals** in the Periodic Table in relation to this line?

Q18   Some elements are known as **semi-metals** or **metalloids**.

a) **Where** are these elements found in the Periodic Table?

b) Give **one example** of a **semi-metal** element.

Q19   One element is **unlike** any other as it is **not** a member of any group. **Name** this element.

Q20   Where are the **transition metals** found on the Periodic Table?

Q21   *Members of Group III form 3+ ions.* What ions do members of **Group II** form?

Q22   What is the **charge** on an ion made from an element in **Group VI**?

Q23   Which is the **most reactive** member of Group I?

Q24   Which is the **most reactive** member of Group II?

Q25   *Sodium has an atomic number of 11 and a mass number of 23.*

          Explain in as much detail as possible what this tells us about an atom of sodium.

Top Tips:

Remember that groups "**group**" things with similar properties, whereas periods show "**periodic variation**" as you cross them — that way you won't forget which is which. You must know how **size** and **reactivity** vary around the table — and make sure you can find your **metals**, **non-metals**, and **noble gases**.

Group 0 — The Noble Gases

Q1   Why are the Noble gases sometimes known as **Group VIII**?

Q2   *The Noble gases are "inert". What does this mean?*

Q3   By referring to their atomic structure, **explain why** the Noble gases are "inert".

Q4   Use the table to **answer** these questions:

a) Why would you expect hydrogen and helium to be **gases** at room temperature and pressure?

	Hydrogen	Helium
Structure of Atom	(H) ×	(He) ×
Boiling Point °C	-253	-269
Melting Point °C	-259	-272
Atomic Number	1	2
Mass Number	2	4

b) For a given number of atoms, which of helium and hydrogen is the **heaviest**?

c) **Write down** the number of protons, electrons and neutrons in an atom of hydrogen and an atom of helium.

d) **Explain why** a sample of helium is more dense than a sample of hydrogen under the same conditions.

e) *If chlorine gas was burnt in hydrogen, a reaction would occur forming hydrogen chloride. What do you think would happen if chlorine was burnt in helium?* **Explain** your answer.

Q5   Why is **helium** used in airships rather than hydrogen?

Q6   **Complete** the paragraph below from the word list.
Words can be used once, more than once, or not at all.

Periodic	inert	1%	Noble	increase	shell	low	full
helium	argon	neon	electrons	radon	radioactive		0

The _____ gases are found in Group_____ on the _____
Table. They are called Noble gases because they do not react with any other
element, as they have a _____ outer _____ of _____.
They are also called the _____ gases. The Noble gases have very
_____ boiling points which _____ down the group. The Noble
gas with the largest atoms is _____ and the one with the smallest atoms
is _____. About _____ of the air is made up of Noble gases.

Q7   *The table below gives information about the Noble gases. Use it to* **answer these questions:**

a) How do the **melting and boiling points** of the gases change as you go down the group?

b) **Complete** the table by estimating the melting point and boiling point of radon.

Noble Gas	Atomic Number	Density at STP g/cm³	Melting Point °C	Boiling Point °C
Helium	2	0.00017	-272	-269
Neon	10	0.00084	-248	-246
Argon	18	0.0016	-189	-186
Krypton	36	0.0034	-157	-153
Xenon	54	0.006	-112	-107
Radon	86	0.01		

c) Why do the **densities** of the Noble gases increase down the group?

Group 0 — The Noble Gases

Q8   Look at the table opposite.

   a) Why do you think the Noble gases proved harder to
   discover than other elements?

   b) *The percentages of noble gases in the air are as follows:*
      Ar 0.93%, Ne 0.0018%, He 0.0005%,
         Kr 0.0001%, Xe 0.0001%.

   Approximately what percentage of air do noble gases make up?

   c) Why may it have been **easier** to discover argon than the other Noble gases?

Element	When discovered
Iron	Ancient times
Helium	1895
Neon	1898
Oxygen	1774
Phosphorus	1669

Q9   Why is neon used in **advertising signs**?

Q10   Give a **common use** for argon and state why it is used for that purpose.

Q11   Why is helium used in **meteorological balloons**, rather than argon?

Neon is Ace!

Q12   *The table below shows some details of the Noble gases.*

   a) **Fill in the gaps** in the table.

   b) **Write down** an element of Group 0 to
      match each of these descriptions:
      i)   Gives out a light when a
           current is passed through it.
      ii) Less dense than air.
      iii) Used in lasers.

Noble Gas	Symbol	Atomic Number	Mass Number	No. of Protons	No. of Electrons	No. of Neutrons
	He		4	2		
Neon			20	10		
	Ar	18	40			
Krypton			84	36		
Xenon		54	131		54	
Radon		86	222			

Q13   **Draw** an atom each of Neon ($^{20}_{10}$Ne) and Argon ($^{40}_{18}$Ar), showing their electronic configurations.

Q14   **Why** would you expect all the elements in Group 0 to have similar properties?

Q15   *When lithium becomes a lithium ion, Li$^+$, it has the same number of electrons as helium.*

   a) **Draw** a lithium ion Li$^+$ and a helium atom, $^4_2$He .

   b) **Label** on each atom the number of protons, neutrons and electrons.

   c) *Although they now have the same electronic configuration, they are
      not the same atom. Why is this?*

Q16   When a potassium atom becomes a potassium ion (K$^+$), it
   has the same electronic configuration as **which** Noble gas?

Q17   Which Noble gases have the same electronic configuration as the following?

   | a) Oxide ion, O^{2-} | | b) Sodium ion, Na$^+$ | | c) Chloride ion, Cl$^-$ |

Q18   If at standard atmospheric pressure argon has a melting point of −189 °C and a boiling
   point of −186 °C, over what temperature ranges would it be a **liquid** and a **gas**?

Top Tips: The thing about noble gases is they **don't do anything**. But you'd better know
why — the examiners like to ask. And don't forget they're all **single-atom** gases. Other than that, just
make sure you know their uses — which are used in **balloons, discharge tubes, bulbs** and **lasers**.

Group I — The Alkali Metals

Q1   *Group 1 of the Periodic Table is known as the **Alkali Metals**.*

a) Why is Group I of the Periodic Table known as the **Alkali Metals**?

b) Why are they known as "**Group I**" in the Periodic Table?

Q2   How are the Alkali metals **stored** and why are they stored this way?

Q3   *Alkali metals react with water to produce a gas and a solution.*

a) What **colour** would the resulting solution be if universal indicator was added?

b) What would be the **pH** of the resulting solution?

Q4   *The table on the right shows four alkali metals and some of their physical properties.*

Alkali Metal	Atomic Mass	Symbol	Boiling Point °C	Melting Point °C	Density g/cm³
Lithium	7		1342	181	0.535
Sodium	23		880	98	0.971
Potassium	39		760	63	0.862
Rubidium	85.5		688	39	1.53

a) Complete the table by filling in their **symbols**.

b) Caesium is the next alkali metal. Estimate its: i) **Boiling point** ii) **Melting point** iii) **Density**.

c) **Explain** why, as you go down Group I, the atoms get **bigger** in cross-section.

d) Which member of the group in the table is the **most dense**?

e) What must become **weaker** for the melting point to decrease down the group?

f) Over what **temperature ranges** would you expect i) Rubidium, ii) Potassium, to be liquids?

Q5   **Explain why** *a freshly cut piece of sodium would have a shiny surface, but after a while it would turn white.*

Q6   **Complete** *the table below, then answer the following questions:*

Alkali Metal	No. of Protons	No. of Neutrons	No. of Electrons	Atomic Number	Mass Number
Lithium				3	7
Sodium	11				23
Potassium	19	20			
Rubidium				37	85
Caesium	55				133

a) **Draw** an atom of sodium showing its electron arrangement.

b) **How many** electrons has sodium in its outer shell?

c) Why does this make sodium so **reactive**?

d) What has to happen to an atom of sodium for it to achieve a **full** outer shell?

e) What is the **charge** of a sodium ion? **Explain** your answer.

f) *When sodium bonds, it changes from an atom to an ion.* What is meant by the term *"ion"*?

Q7   *Shown below are two diagrams of atoms.*

a) **Complete** the atoms by adding the correct number of electrons in each shell.

b) How can lithium and potassium **gain** a full outer shell of electrons?

c) What would the **charge** on the ions be?

d) **Write** the **symbol** for each ion formed.

e) *In general, the further away the outer electron from the nucleus, the easier it is to remove.* Which of lithium and potassium would you expect to be **more reactive**? Explain your answer.

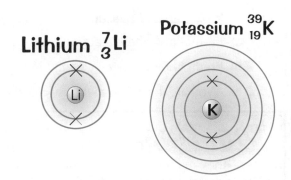

Group I — The Alkali Metals

Q8   Put the metals in the box in order of reactivity — the most reactive first.

> Caesium, Potassium, Lithium, Sodium, Rubidium.

Q9   Match up the alkali metal to its reaction in water:

A) Potassium	**1) Ignites with yellow/orange flame, fizzes vigorously.**
B) Sodium	**2) No flame, but fizzes.**
C) Lithium	**3) Pops and ignites with a lilac flame, fizzes very vigorously.**

Q10   *When an alkali metal reacts with water, a gas is produced.*

a) **Name** the gas that is produced.

b) How could you test for this gas?

c) **Complete** the equations to the right.

Sodium + Water → ▢

Lithium + Water → ▢

d) i) **Complete** and **balance** this equation: $K_{(s)} + H_2O_{(l)} \rightarrow KOH_{(aq)} +$ ▢

ii) What do the symbols (s), (l), (aq), and (g) stand for in chemical equations?

Q11   Name **two ions** present in an aqueous solution of potassium hydroxide.

Q12   *Lithium burns in air to form lithium oxide.*

a) i) Using the diagrams, **explain** how this happens.

ii) **Write** the formula of the compound lithium oxide.

iii) **Complete** the equations below and balance them:

Lithium + oxygen → ▢		Li + O₂ → ▢	
Sodium + oxygen → ▢		Na + O₂ → ▢	

b) All the alkali metals in Group I would react in a similar way with oxygen and water. **Explain** why this is so.

Q13   **Complete** the table below with the given words and sentences.

> tarnishes quickly to give an oxide layer   tarnishes slowly to give oxide layer
> tarnishes very quickly to give oxide layer

	Reaction of the Metal in Air
Lithium	
Sodium	
Potassium	

Q14   Rubidium and caesium are very dangerous.

a) **Predict** how these react with **water**.

b) **Predict** how these react with **air**.

c) Why are these two metals so reactive?

Top Tips: With only **one** electron in their outer shell, these metals **don't have much to** lose — they're pretty **reactive**. The Exam's most likely to ask about **trends** in the group — make sure you know how **size**, **reactivity**, **density** and **melting** and **boiling points** vary down the group — and **why**.

Group VII — The Halogens

Q1   Why are the halogens known as the Group VII elements?

Q2   Complete the table below and answer the questions.

Halogen	Number of electrons in outer shell	State at room temperature	Colour at room temperature	Symbol
Fluorine	7			
Chlorine		gas		
Bromine			brown	
Iodine				I

a) Bromine is a brown volatile liquid. What is meant by **volatile**?

b) Why are the atoms **bigger** as you go **down** the group?

c) How does the **reactivity** change down the group?

Q3   Under atmospheric pressure, chlorine's melting point is –101 °C, and its boiling point is –35 °C. Between what temperatures would chlorine be **a)** a Solid **b)** a Liquid **c)** a Gas?

Q4   *Look at the information in the table.*

a) From the information given, **estimate** the melting point of iodine.

b) **Describe** the patterns (trends) in the melting and boiling points down the group.

Halogen	Melting Point °C	Boiling Point °C
Fluorine	-220	-188
Chlorine	-101	-35
Bromine	-7	58
Iodine		184

Q5   *Fluorine is an atom with this chemical symbol* $\rightarrow {}^{19}_{9}F$

a) **Draw** an atom of fluorine from the information given.

b) On your diagram **write down** i) the number of protons   ii) the number of neutrons
iii) the number of electrons   iv) the electronic configuration.

Q6   *All the halogens form molecules which are pairs of atoms.*
Write the formula for: i) the chlorine molecule   ii) the iodine molecule.

Q7   *The diagram on the left shows an atom of chlorine.*

a) **Draw** a **molecule** of chlorine using this atom to help you.

b) What type of bonding do we call this?

Atom of Chlorine

Q8   *The Halogens also form another type of bond by gaining one electron.*

a) What is this type of bonding called?

b) What would be the charge on a halogen ion?

c) **Name** a compound in which chlorine would gain an electron.

d) **Name** a compound in which chlorine would share an electron.

Q9   **Draw** the atomic structure and write the **names of the compounds** formed when:

a) Fluorine combines with lithium,   **b)** Chlorine combines with hydrogen.

Q10   **State** what type of bonding is found in the following halogen compounds:

a) Hydrogen fluoride, HF **b)** Lithium chloride, LiCl **c)** Tetrachloromethane **d)** Potassium bromide. **How can you tell** the type of bonding in each? Is there a general rule you followed?

Q11   Fill in the spaces to **complete** this table:

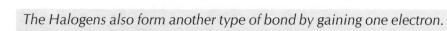

Halogen	Symbol	No. of Protons	No. of Neutrons	No. of Electrons	Atomic Mass	Atomic Number
Fluorine	F				19	9
Chlorine	Cl	17	18		35	
Bromine	Br	35			80	
Iodine	I				127	53
Astatine	At	85			210	

Group VII — The Halogens

Q12 *The reactivity of the halogens decreases down the group, but the reactivity of the alkali metals increases down the group.* **Explain** *this difference.*

H Q13 *Iodine can change easily from a dark grey solid to a purple vapour. It does not become a liquid. What do we call this change?*

Q14 *Halogens react with metals to form salts.*

   a) What is a salt?

   b) Given that Halogens are poisonous, where should reactions of metals and halogens be carried out?

   c) Write in the salts formed from the following reactions:

   d) Are the salts ionic or covalent compounds? **Explain** your answer.

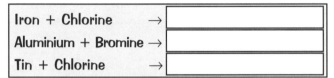

Iron + Chlorine	→	
Aluminium + Bromine	→	
Tin + Chlorine	→	

Q15 *Most halides are soluble, but* **silver halides** *are not (e.g. silver chloride). They can be used to test for halide salts because they produce coloured insoluble precipitates.*

   a) What does the term **"precipitate"** mean?

   b) What symbol shows a precipitate in a reaction?

   c) Match the silver halide to the colour of the precipitate formed:

   d) *Look at the reaction below.*

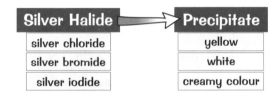

Silver Halide	Precipitate
silver chloride	yellow
silver bromide	white
silver iodide	creamy colour

> Silver nitrate + Sodium chloride → Silver chloride + Sodium nitrate

   Write equations for the reaction of **silver nitrate** *with:* i) **sodium bromide** ii) **sodium iodide.**

Q16 What effect will chlorine gas have on damp, blue litmus paper?

Q17 *You are given a sample of a solid compound marked X, and told it is a halide salt.* **Explain** *how you could carry out an experiment to find which halide is present in X.*

Q18 *Chlorine is bubbled through sodium bromide as shown in the diagram.*

   a) What would you see happening in the test tube?

   b) Which of chlorine or bromine is the most reactive?

   c) How can you **explain** the results of the reaction?

   d) Write an equation to explain the reaction.

   e) Complete the equations below by writing the symbols and balancing them.

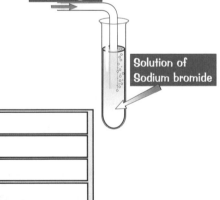

Chlorine gas

Solution of Sodium bromide

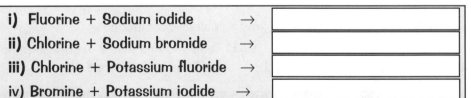

i) Fluorine + Sodium iodide	→	
ii) Chlorine + Sodium bromide	→	
iii) Chlorine + Potassium fluoride	→	
iv) Bromine + Potassium iodide	→	

Top Tips:
The halogens' reactivity varies in the **opposite** way to group I — make sure you understand **why**. And learn how **size, colour** and **melting and boiling points** vary down the group. Then all you need to know is their **dangers**, how you'd **test** for them, and their **displacement reactions**. Nice.

Transition Metals

Q1 *The transition metals have properties of typical metals.*

List the properties you would expect a transition element to have.

Q2 Name **four** transition metals you might come across everyday and where you would find them.

Q3 *The transition metals form a block in the Periodic Table, rather than fall into groups like the other elements.*

Where are they found in the Periodic Table?

Q4 *A metal "X" has a high melting point, can form 2⁺ or 3⁺ ions, and reacts slowly over a long time with water.*

a) **Explain why** you would put this in the transition element block rather than in Group II.

b) This same metal X forms coloured compounds with oxygen. **Write the formula** for the combination of this metal with oxygen to form:

i) X(II) Oxide   **ii)** X (III) Oxide

Q5 **Match** the correct colour to each of these compounds:

1) Chromium compounds	**A) White**
2) Manganese compounds	**B) Yellow / orange**
3) Copper compound	**C) Blue**
4) Magnesium compounds	**D) Purple**
5) Sodium compounds	**E) White**

Q6 *Human blood contains iron and is red.*

a) What **colour** would you expect Fe_2O_3 to be?

b) Some species of spiders' blood contains copper, what **colour** might it be?

Q7 *The transition metal elements often have more than just one ion. For example, iron can be Iron(II) — Fe^{2+} or Iron(III) — Fe^{3+}. The number in brackets refers to the metal ion charge.*

Write the formula for the following compounds in the table and give the charge on the transition element ion in each case. One has been done for you.

(use the ion table on the inside front cover)

Compound	Formula	Charge on Ion
a) Iron(II) oxide		
b) Iron(III) chloride		
c) Iron(III) bromide	$FeBr_3$	Fe^{3+}
d) Copper(II) oxide		
e) Copper(I) chloride		
f) Copper(II) chloride		
g) Iron(III) iodide		

Q8 *Iron(II) can be easily changed into Iron(III) : Fe^{3+}*

a) What **type** of reaction is this?

b) What type of reaction would it be if Fe^{3+} ions were **changed** into Fe^{2+} ions?

Transition Metals

Q9   *Answer these questions on the uses of transition metals:*

a) **Give a use** for each of these transition metals: i) Iron ii) Zinc iii) Copper

b) Why is copper used for household water pipes in **preference** to iron or zinc?

Q10   **Name two** transition elements that could be made into a permanent magnet.

Q11   *An element Y was discovered and put with the transition metals because of its properties.*

a) **Fill in the table** below for the element Y, giving details of its
general properties (in terms of good, bad, high, low, etc.).

Conductivity		Density	Malleability	Melting pt
Heat	Electricity			

b) *It was found that element Y formed 2 ions, Y^+ and Y^{2+}, so it can be used to make a variety of compounds.*   **Write down** the formulae of the following compounds for the element Y:
i) Y(I) chloride   **ii)** Y(I) oxide   **iii)** Y(II) oxide

Q12   *Most of the transition elements are used to form alloys to improve their physical or chemical properties or to combine useful properties.*
What do you think the following alloys could be **used** for?

a) Titanium alloy *(light, strong and resistant to corrosion)*?

b) Iron in the form of stainless steel: 70% iron, 20% chromium, 10% nickel *(hard and does not rust)*?

c) Bronze: 90% copper, 10% tin *(harder than just pure copper)*?

Q13   *It is possible to change copper sulphate crystals from blue to white.*

a) What substance are you **removing** by turning them into white crystals?

b) **How** could you remove this substance?

c) What would you **call** this white powdered form of copper sulphate?

d) *The white powder will return to a blue colour if the removed substance is replaced.*
Give a laboratory **use** for this reaction.

Q14   *The transition elements and some of their compounds make good catalysts.*

a) What is a **catalyst**?

b) Match up each transition element **catalyst** to its **function**:

A) Nickel	1) Haber process
B) Iron	2) Decomposition of hydrogen peroxide
C) Manganese(IV) oxide	3) Turning oils into fats

Top Tip
Catalysts with **colourful compounds** — that about sums up **transition** metals. They mainly vary in their **inner** electrons only — so they're all pretty **similar chemically**. Make sure you know a couple of **examples** of catalyst reactions — and can name uses for **iron, copper** and **zinc**.

Metals

Q1   *Melting and boiling points of metals are generally high.*

   a) How does this make them useful?

   b) Which metal is the main exception to this? Give one use of it because of this property.

Q2   *Metals are malleable. What does **malleable** mean and where could this property be useful?*

Q3   *In a laboratory, the tensile strength of metals can be tested.*

   a) Explain a simple test you would use. What precautions would you need to take?

   b) How could you ensure it was a **fair** test?

Q4   **Match up** each metal to its use:

1. Copper	A. Used for jewellery
2. Lead	B. Used for aircraft
3. Aluminium	C. Used for wiring
4. Gold	D. Used to keep out radiation

Q5 **a)** Complete the table below, showing properties and associated uses for the above four metals. The first one has been done for you.

Metal	Property	Use
Copper	Conducts electricity	Household wiring
Lead		
Aluminium		
Gold		

   b) What is the name given to a **mixture of metals**?

   c) Why do we mix metals together?

   d) How is this done?

   e) Why is this called a mixture and **not** a compound?

Q6   *Using the table opposite answer these questions:*

   a) Explain why tungsten is used in light bulbs.

   b) Draw a bar chart showing the melting points of the metals in the table.

Metal	Melting Point (°C)
Aluminium	659
Copper	1083
Gold	1064
Iron	1540
Lead	328
Tin	232
Tungsten	3410

Q7   How does the **pH** of metallic oxides compare to that of non-metallic oxides?

Q8   **Explain why** gold does not tarnish easily and is found as an element on its own.

Top Tips:

Metallic bonding's due to **free electrons** — and the bonds are usually pretty **strong**. Make sure you understand how this affects their conduction of **heat** and **electricity** — and their **melting and boiling points**. Other than that, just make sure you can define an **alloy** — and give **examples**.

Non-Metals

Q1   *Look at the Periodic Table opposite.*

Shade in the area that
represents non-metals.

Q2   *Iron is a metal and sulphur is a non-metal.*

Complete the table below for both, showing the differences
between metals and non-metals. Use the words in the box.

poor conductor	low	good conductor
malleable	high	brittle

Element	Conducts heat	Conducts electricity	Melting Point	Boiling Point	Strength	Density
Iron						
Sulphur						

Q3   *Most non-metals do not conduct electricity.*

a) What is the general name given to non-conducting materials?

b) Explain why non-metals **do not** conduct electricity.

c) Name an **exception** to this rule.

Q4   **Answer** *these questions on bondings between non-metal elements:*

a) What type of **bonding** do you get between two non-metal elements?

b) **Explain** why this is so.

Q5   *Non-metals form small molecules whilst metals bond in giant metallic structures.*

Give two **properties** that each have because of their structures.

Q6   *Hydrogen is a non-metal. The structure of an atom of hydrogen is drawn below.*

*Hydrogen is a gas at room temperature and pressure, and it shares a number
of properties with non-metals. However, it could be argued that hydrogen
be placed in **Group I** of the Periodic Table. **Explain** why this is so.*

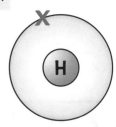

Q7   What type of **bonding** does hydrogen form with oxygen?

Q8   *Carbon and iodine sublime.*

What does this **mean?**

Non-Metals

Q9   *Look at the diagrams of two atoms.*

a) **Complete** the diagrams by adding crosses to the outer shell of each atom.

b) *Oxygen forms an ionic bond with a metal.*

What type of charge will the oxygen ion have?

c) *Carbon and oxygen join together as two non-metals to form the covalent molecule carbon dioxide (CO_2).* **Draw** a dot and cross electron diagram of carbon dioxide.

Q10   *Look at the table below of the melting points across one period of the Periodic Table.*

Element	Sodium	Magnesium	Aluminium	Silicon	Phosphorus	Sulphur	Chlorine	Argon
Atomic Number	11	12	13	14	15	16	17	18
Melting Point (°C)	100	620	630	1400	30	110	-100	-190

a) Using the table, **plot a graph** of the melting points against atomic number across the period.

b) **Explain** any trends you see in your graph.

c) Are there any results that seem unusual. **Suggest a reason** for this.

d) Using your knowledge of atomic structure which element listed would you expect to have the **weakest attraction** between atoms? Why?

Q11   *Silicon and carbon can form giant structures.*

Why is this unusual for non-metals?

Q12   *These two diagrams show the structures of graphite and diamond (two forms of carbon):*

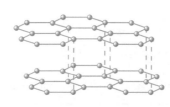

a) *Graphite and diamond show different properties.*
Giving reasons, state which of the two you think show the following properties:

   i) Conducts electricity.   ii) Is a hard material.   iii) Is a soft material.

b) Give one industrial use of diamond and one industrial use of graphite.

Q13   *Non-metal oxides such as SO_2 and NO_2 are often released into the atmosphere.*

a) What **substances** would these make if mixed with water?

b) Why is their release into the atmosphere a problem, and what's the common name for this phenomenon?

Top Tips:

Exams questions often compare **non-metals** with metals. Just make sure you understand **why** non-metals are made of **molecules** — and **how** this affects their **properties**. And you must know how and why **diamond** and **graphite** differ.

Acids and Alkalis

Q1 Place a **tick** in the box next to each of the following statements to indicate which are **True** and which are **False**.

Is it True or must it be False...

	True	False
All acids are dangerous		
All alkalis are dangerous		
Acids produce H^+ ions in solution		
Alkalis produce OH^- ions in solution		

Is it True, or by its very nature must it therefore be False...

	True	False
Acids have a pH above 7		
Acids have a pH below 7		
The pH scale goes from 0 to 14		

Q2 Give the names of three common bench acids and alkalis, and write out their formulae:

Name of Acid	Formula of Acid		Name of Alkali	Formula of Alkali
(i)			(i)	
(ii)			(ii)	
(iii)			(iii)	

Q3 What do we call a substance with a **pH** of 7?

Q4 Name a substance that is usually pH 7.

Q5 State which of the following is an **acid** and which is an **alkali**:

a) Hydrochloric acid	b) Sodium hydroxide	c) KOH	d) H_2SO_4	e) HNO_3

Q6 What is an **indicator**?

Q7 Why are indicators useful?

Q8 What is a base? Name three bases.

Q9 Complete the table by adding the correct colour of the indicator in acid or alkali:

Indicator	Colour in solution of:	
	Acid	Alkali
Universal Indicator		
Red Litmus		
Blue Litmus		
Phenolphthalein		
Methyl Orange		
Methyl Red		

Acids and Alkalis

Q10 Colour in the pH chart with the correct colours for Universal indicator solution:

pH 1 2 3 4 5 6 7 8 9 10 11 12 13 14

ACIDS   ALKALIS

←   NEUTRAL   →

Q11 What values of pH would you expect for .....?

i) Citric acid   **iv)** Oven cleaner

ii) Sodium chloride (common salt)   **v)** Sodium hydroxide

iii) Lime (calcium hydroxide)   **vi)** Hydrochloric acid

Q12 Fill in the blanks with the correct words:

Universal indicator turns a _____ colour in strong acids,
_____ in neutral solutions and _____ in strong alkalis.
Another indicator which changes colour in acid and alkali is _____ .
A solution which is not acid or alkali is said to be _____, and has a
pH of _____ .
Lemons and oranges contain _____ acid.
Fizzy drinks contain _____ acid.
Taking milk of magnesia tablets may help indigestion because they
contain a weak _____ . Strong oven cleaners contain a strong
alkali called _____ _____ .
Car batteries contain _____ acid.

Q13 Explain how you could **measure** the pH of a colourless solution.

Q14 Explain how you could **measure** the pH of a brightly-coloured solution.

Q15 *The labels have fallen off test tubes of vinegar, water, sulphuric
acid, and oven cleaner. The table to the right shows the colours
observed when pH paper was added to each tube.*

Fill in the missing **pH values** and **identify**
which substance is in which tube.

Tube	Colour	pH
1	Red	
2	Orange	
3	Green	
4	Blue	

Top Tips:
This stuff's not so bad, I'd say — just loads of **H⁺** and **OH⁻** ions floating
about. But make sure you can define an **acid** and **alkali** in terms of these — and write an equation
for their **neutralisation**. If you can do that and know your **pH scale**, you're pretty much there...

Acid Reactions

Q1   Complete the following general acid reactions by filling in the missing products.

> Acid + Base → A Salt + _____
>
> Acid + Metal → A Salt + _____
>
> Acid + Metal Carbonate → A Salt + Water + _____ _____
>
> Acid + Metal Hydrogencarbonate → A _____ + Water + Carbon dioxide

Q2   What is an alkali?

Q3   What is a base?

Q4   **Give** a **definition** of a salt.

Q5   **Link up** the words in the diagram opposite to show the salt produced by each acid.

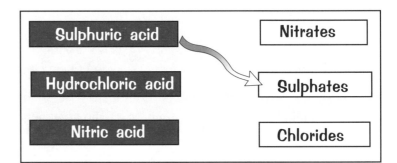

Q6   Write out the **products** of the following reactions. **H** Then complete the **formulae** for the compounds and **balance** the equation. Here is an example completed for you:

Hydrochloric Acid + Sodium Hydroxide → Sodium Chloride + Water
H   HCl   +   NaOH   →   NaCl   + H_2O

a) Hydrochloric acid + Potassium hydroxide →
   H

b) Hydrochloric acid + Calcium hydroxide →
   H

c) Sulphuric acid + Potassium hydroxide →
   H

d) Hydrochloric acid + Calcium carbonate →
   H

e) Hydrochloric acid + Zinc →
   H

f) Nitric acid + Sodium hydroxide →
   H

g) Nitric acid + Sodium hydrogencarbonate →
   H

h) Phosphoric acid + Ammonium hydroxide →
   H H_3PO_4 +   →   + $(NH_4)_3PO_4$

i) Hydrochloric acid + Sodium oxide →
   H

Acid Reactions

Q7 **Answer** these questions on neutralisation:

a) What is neutralisation?

b) Why is neutralisation important to farmers?

c) What do farmers use to neutralise over-acidic soils?

Q8 *Two companies advertise pills which they say relieve stomach ache by neutralising excess stomach acid.*

a) **Describe** what you would do to:

i) check that the pills do in fact neutralise acid?

ii) discover which pill neutralised the most acid?

b) *Magnesium Hydroxide is the active ingredient in some indigestion tablets.* **Write** an equation showing how this chemical reacts with acid in the stomach.

Q9 *Read the following passage, which explains how fire extinguishers work.*

> *Red fire extinguishers contain sodium hydrogencarbonate solution. When the plunger is pressed down, sulphuric acid mixes and reacts with the sodium hydrogencarbonate solution, causing a gas to be produced. This makes the pressure build up inside the cylinder, forcing a foam of liquid and bubbles to be squeezed out of the nozzle.*

a) What is the name of the gas?

b) **Write** a word equation to show what happens.

Q10 Use the information opposite to **suggest** the best remedy for:

a) a wasp sting   b) a bee sting   c) nettle sting.

- Wasp stings are basic.
- Bee stings are acidic.
- Nettles stings are acidic.
- Bicarbonate of soda is alkaline.
- Dock leaves contain alkali.
- Lemon juice is acidic.

H Q11 Neutralisation is simplified as $H^+_{(aq)} + OH^-_{(aq)} \rightarrow H_2O_{(l)}$

Explain where the H^+ and OH^- come from.

Q12 Which acid and which other chemical would you use to make ..... ?

a) Sodium chloride   b) Copper chloride   c) Potassium sulphate

d) Zinc sulphate   e) Ammonium nitrate   f) Ammonium sulphate

Q13 Why is it a **bad idea** to use sodium and hydrochloric acid to make sodium chloride?

Top Tips:

These reactions seem a bit complicated — but there's basically only **four types**. If you can write equations for **bases**, **metals**, **metal carbonates** and **metal hydrogencarbonates**, you'll sail through. Make sure you can work out the **salt** produced when something's **neutralised** — write out the equation if you're not sure.

The Reactivity Series of Metals

Q1   *The reactivity series is a list of metals.*

a) What do you **understand** by the term "reactivity series"?

b) Some metals corrode in air. What is meant by **corrosion**?

c) *Metals react with air, water and acids. What might you look for in such reactions to identify which is* the **most reactive** metal?

d) Put these metals in order of reactivity, starting with the most reactive first:

| potassium | gold | aluminium | silver | lead | sodium | iron | copper | zinc |

e) **Match** the following metals to the correct statement.

1) Potassium	A) Will not react with water or dilute acid
2) Copper	B) Found alone not combined with anything
3) Iron	C) Very reactive metal
4) Gold	D) Corrodes in air fairly easily forming a substance called rust

Q2   Between which elements are i) carbon and ii) hydrogen, in the reactivity series?

Q3   *Potassium has one electron in its outer shell, which is lost easily.*

a) Whereabouts in the **reactivity series** would you expect to find potassium?

b) **Name** two elements that could be above potassium in the reactivity series.

c) Using the information given below, **place** metals X and Y
   in the correct position in the reactivity series to the right.

> **Metal X —**   Very reactive, burns in air readily to form a
>   layer of oxide. Reacts violently in water
>   but does not ignite the hydrogen produced.
>
> **Metal Y —**   Corrodes very slowly, needs carbon for
>   extraction from ore.

> Potassium
> Magnesium
> Iron
> Gold
> Platinum

Q4   *Look at the following:*   **Sodium** $^{23}_{11}$**Na** , **Magnesium** $^{24}_{12}$**Mg**

a) **Draw** an atom of sodium and magnesium.
   How many electrons has each to **lose** to gain a full shell?

b) Looking at the atomic structure of these metals, **why** is
   magnesium less reactive than sodium?

The Reactivity Series of Metals

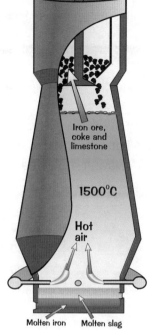

Iron ore, coke and limestone

1500°C

Hot air

Molten iron   Molten slag

Q5   *The diagram on the right shows the Blast Furnace used to convert iron ore to iron. Coke burns to form CO_2 which then reacts with more coke to make carbon monoxide. The carbon monoxide is a reducing agent and reacts with iron ore (Fe_2O_3) to make iron.*
$$Fe_2O_3 + 3CO \rightarrow 2Fe + 3CO_2$$

a) What is a **reducing agent**?

b) **Where** is carbon in the reactivity series relative to iron?

c) **Explain** how the carbon monoxide reduces the iron ore.

d) **Write** a word equation for the reaction given above.

Q6   *Silver, gold and platinum are found **native in** the ground as elements and not as compounds.*

Explain how this can happen.

Q7   *Aluminium is much more **abundant** in the Earth's crust than iron, yet it is much **more expensive** to buy.*

Explain why it is so expensive, in terms of its reactivity and the cost of extracting it from its ore.

Q8   Why do you think gold and silver can be worn next to the skin as jewellery, but other metals like sodium cannot?

Q9   *Metals are shiny. They do however become "dull" with time.*

a) **Name** a metal that would become **dull** if left in air for only a short time.

b) **Name** a metal that would **not** become **dull** easily in air.

c) **Write down** the name of the product in (**a**).

Q10   *The table opposite contains information about metals.*

a) **Complete the table**, using your own words to explain what happens when each metal is heated in air.

b) **Write** a balanced equation for the reaction of the following with air (you'll need to work out which element in the air they react with first):

i) Iron.

ii) Calcium.

iii) Sodium.

c) From your results in (**a**) **write a list** of the order of reactivity, starting with the most reactive.

Metal	Reaction when heated in air	Compound formed
Calcium		
Zinc		
Iron		
Copper	slow reaction	
Silver		
Potassium		
Gold		
Magnesium		
Platinum	no reaction	
Lead		

Top Tips:

A metal's **reactivity** is just how easily its atoms **lose electrons**. It's pretty handy though — so make sure you know it. If you can use it to predict **displacement reactions** then you've pretty much got it sussed. Thinking up a **rhyme** or **mnemonic** will help you remember it — so try this if you find it hard.

Industrial Salt

Q1 State the main **use** of solid rock salt, especially important in the **winter months**?

Q2 Where are large **salt deposits** found in the UK?

Q3 What is the **common name** for concentrated sodium chloride solution?

Q4 *Heating increases the amount of salt that can be dissolved in a given volume of water.*

   a) What is a **saturated solution**?

   b) *The graph shows the solubility of two salts.*

   Which salt is the most soluble at: **i) low temperatures**   **ii) high temperatures.**

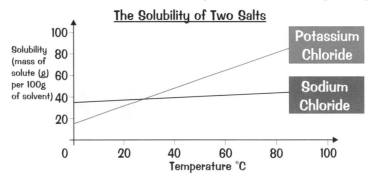

Q5 *Sodium hydroxide is obtained from rock salt industrially by electrolysis.* What is **electrolysis**?

Q6 *Sodium chloride is made into a solution before it is electrolysed.*

   a) What is this **solution** called?

   b) Why does sodium chloride have to be made into a solution **before** electrolysis?

Q7 Label the diagram opposite showing the electrolysis of a solution of sodium chloride. Use the following labels:

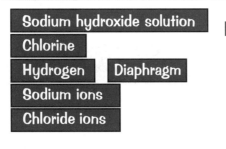

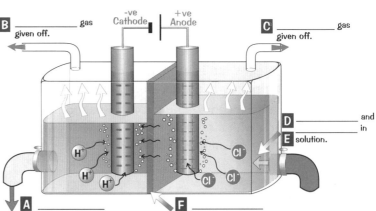

Q8 In this electrolysis process why is sodium **not** produced at the cathode?

Q9 **Draw** the electronic structure of the following transformation occurring during the electrolysis of sodium chloride:

   Chloride ion → Chlorine atom

Q10 *Look at the equations below.* Are they **oxidation** or **reduction** reactions?

   i) $Cl^- \rightarrow Cl + e^-$ **ii)** $H^+ + e^- \rightarrow H$

Uses of Halogens and Salt Products

Q1   *Chlorine is used in bleach. Bleach is made by dissolving chlorine in sodium hydroxide solution.*

This is the reaction:

$$Cl_{2(g)} + NaOH_{(aq)} \rightarrow NaOCl_{(aq)} + NaCl_{(aq)} + H_2O_{(l)}$$

Balance the equation.

Q2   Give **two** other uses of chlorine.

Q3   *Chlorine is used in the manufacture of hydrogen chloride. When Hydrogen chloride is dissolved in water, a solution of hydrochloric acid is formed.*

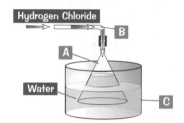

The diagram shows the hydrogen chloride gas being dissolved in water to make hydrochloric acid.

a) **Name** the pieces of apparatus A, B and C.

b) What **ion** must be present to make the solution of hydrogen chloride acidic?

Q4   **a)** **Explain** why bromine does not combine with hydrogen as readily as chlorine.

b) How easily would you expect **iodine** to combine with hydrogen?

Q5   *Chlorine and bromine are both **oxidising agents**. This means that they **cause oxidation** (the loss of electrons).*

a) Why do they "**want**" to oxidise other chemicals?

b) *Chlorine is a **stronger oxidising agent** than bromine.* Explain **why** it is stronger.

c) **Complete** the equations:

i) $Cl_2 + $ _____ $\rightarrow 2Cl^-$

ii) $Br_2 + $ _____ $\rightarrow 2Br^-$

Q6   Why is **fluoride** added to drinking water? What other product might have fluoride added?

Q7   *Iodine is less reactive than fluorine, chlorine and bromine.*

a) Would it make a good **oxidising** agent?

b) What is **iodine** used for?

Q8   *Silver halides are used in photographic film. A sample of silver bromide can be made from a mixture of silver nitrate and sodium bromide.*

a) *The silver bromide (AgBr) formed is easy to split apart.* **Write an equation** to show this.

b) Which type of **energy** splits up the silver bromide in photography?

Rates of Reaction

Q1 **Place** these chemical reactions **in order** of their speed, starting with the fastest reaction:

> Frying an egg   Striking a match   A car rusting   Concrete setting   Digesting food

Q2 *When measuring the rate of a chemical reaction you can measure either the disappearance of reactant or the production of the product. Look at the apparatus below:*

A 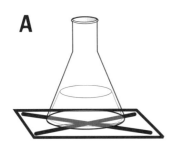 **B** 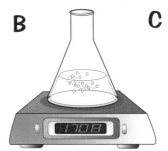 **C**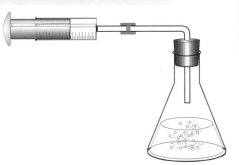

For each reaction below, say which of the apparatus above could be used.

> **a)** Marble chips with hydrochloric acid

> **b)** Magnesium and sulphuric acid

> **c)** Sodium thiosulphate and hydrochloric acid

Q3 Which of the statements below are **true** and which must be **false**?

	True	False
Catalysts are used up in reactions		
Catalysts are specific to certain reactions		
Enzymes are biological catalysts		
Reactions slow if catalysts are used		
Enzymes increase the activation energy		

	True	False
Reactions will speed up if they are heated		
Reactions slow down if they are diluted		
Increasing concentration increases the rate of reaction		
Pressure increases the rates of gaseous reactions		
Reactions are fast at the start		

Q4 *The following changes may speed up the rate of a chemical reaction between an* **acid** *and* **magnesium**.

Put a tick in the box next to each one that will **SPEED UP** the reaction (assume that there is initially an excess of acid).

> A) Heating the acid...
>
> B) Using more-concentrated acid...
>
> C) Using powdered metal, not ribbon...
>
> D) Using twice the volume of acid...
>
> E) Using a suitable catalyst...
>
> F) Adding more magnesium...

Q5 **Describe** a simple reaction that could be studied by monitoring the rate at which the **product** is formed.

Q6 *Reactions can be monitored by looking at how the mass of reactants decreases.*

Describe a simple reaction that could be studied in this manner.

Rates of Reaction

Q7 *Products are produced at a rate shown by a rate curve.*

a) On the axes opposite **draw** a **typical rate curve**.

b) Place on the **curve** the following labels concerning the reaction rate:

(A) FAST

(B) SLOWING

(C) STOPPED

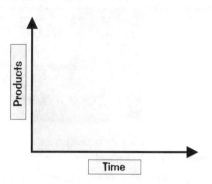

c) For a reaction to occur reacting particles must bump into each other with enough energy to cause a reaction. Imagine a reaction where two chemicals ⬤ and ⬤ collide to react. The product would be ⬤⬤

The reaction would therefore be: ⬤ + ⬤ ⟶ ⬤⬤

Look at stages **A-C** of a reaction below.

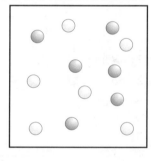 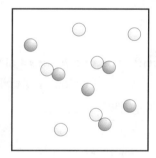 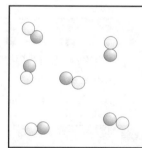

Reaction			

Speed			

Complete the diagrams by placing the following labels below the correct pictures.

END	**MIDDLE**	**START**
STOPPED	**FAST**	**SLOWING**

Ⓐ Ⓑ Ⓒ

Q8 *Reacting particles do not always collide **properly** or **effectively**. Sometimes they miss or collide as described opposite.*

Complete the diagram to show what might be happening to the particles in each case.

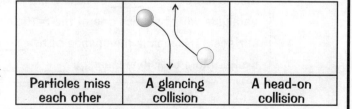

Particles miss each other	A glancing collision	A head-on collision

Top Tips:

Well, there's **four** things that affect the **rates of reactions** — learning your **collision theory** should take care of that. Then it's just a case of learning the **three** ways of **monitoring** reaction rates. Just be sure you can **explain** them — and can draw a **graph** of the results against time for each of them.

Collision Theory

Q1 Use your knowledge of reaction rates to **fill in** the blanks below.
Then put the correct labels on the diagrams.

> **Fill the blank words (use more than once)**
> moderate   surface area   faster   collide
> particles catalyst   collision theory
> concentration   energy   more often
> successful   collision

> **Diagram labels**
> FAST   SLOW   HIGH CONCENTRATION
> LOW CONCENTRATION   LARGE
> SURFACE AREA   CATALYST PRESENT

Particles can only react if they _____ with enough _____ for the reaction to take place.
This is called the _____ _____. There are four factors that can change the rate of a
chemical reaction; temperature, _____, surface area and the use of a suitable _____.

Temperature

Increasing the temperature will cause the particles to move
_____, with more energy. They will therefore
collide _____ _____and with greater
_____. These two things mean there are more
successful collisions per second and therefore a
_____ rate of reaction.

Concentration

Increasing the concentration of a reactant simply means
there are more _____ which may collide and so
react. More collisions means a _____ reaction.

Surface Area

Using a powder instead of a lump means the _____
_____ is greater, which means a greater area of
reactant is exposed and so available for a collision.
More collisions means a _____ reaction.

Catalysts

Use of a suitable catalyst means that the particles may
react even if they collide with only _____ energy. This
means more _____ collisions are likely. Some
catalysts work because one of the particles is fixed to a
surface. This makes the chance of a _____ more
likely. More collisions means a _____ reaction.

Q2 *Match* the three descriptions below to these three diagrams:

A. The particles brush past each other and collide only gently.

B. The particles are separated by a barrier and do not collide.

C. The particles collide energetically with each other.

Collision Theory

Q3   Choose **the sentence** that **best describes** the collision theory:

   a) Particles collide at random and always react.

   b) Collisions between particles often result in a reaction.

   c) Reacting particles must collide with enough energy in order to react.

   d) Collisions between molecules are sometimes needed before a reaction occurs.

Collision Theory 2:
It's not the falling that hurts, it's the landing.

Q4   *Four factors may have an effect on the rate of reaction.*
   Match each one with the explanation of how it works.

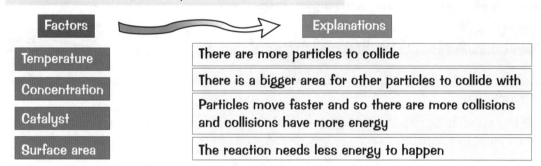

Factors	Explanations
Temperature	There are more particles to collide
Concentration	There is a bigger area for other particles to collide with
Catalyst	Particles move faster and so there are more collisions and collisions have more energy
Surface area	The reaction needs less energy to happen

Q5   *This apparatus may be used to investigate the reaction between marble chips and dilute hydrochloric acid. Some marble chips are left unreacted at the end.*

A graph showing the results from such an experiment is shown on the right.

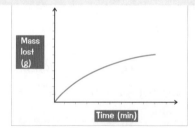

Here are four other graphs plotted to the same scale:

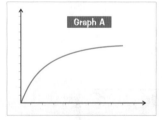
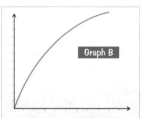
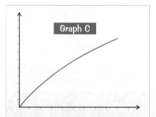
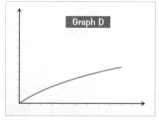

   a) Referring to the original graph, **match each** of the graphs **A-D** with the correct description:

   i) the same volume of acid but twice as concentrated.

   ii) the same concentration of acid but twice the volume.

   iii) the same mass of marble chips but smaller chips.

   iv) the same volume and concentration of ice-cold acid.

   b) Use the theory of collisions to explain each of your answers to parts i) → iv).

Top Tips:

This collision theory stuff is what I call **real** science — **and** it makes sense — things only **react** if they collide with enough speed — anything that increases their **speed** or **number of collisions** will increase the rate. Make sure you know how it applies to **temperature, concentration, surface area** and **catalysts**.

Experiments on Rates of Reaction

Q1 *The reaction between sodium thiosulphate and hydrochloric acid produces a yellow precipitate of solid sulphur. This makes the solution cloudy and prevents us seeing clearly through it. The cross below the flask in the diagram will slowly disappear as the sulphur is produced.*

In an experiment to investigate rates of reaction, the time taken for the cross to disappear was recorded.

50cm³ of sodium thiosulphate solution was used and 10cm³ of hydrochloric acid was added.

The experiment was repeated at different temperatures.

Temperature (°C)	20	30	40	50	60	70
Time taken (s)	163	87	43	23	11	5

a) Use these results to **plot a graph**, with time taken on the vertical axis and temperature on the horizontal axis.

b) **Use the graph** to draw a simple conclusion about the effect of temperature on the time taken for the reaction to finish.

c) The rate of a reaction may be found by dividing 1 by the time taken (1/t). **Work out** the rate at each of the above temperatures.

d) **Plot a graph** of rate against temperature *(If the actual numbers for the rate value are too small to plot, use 'Rate x 1000' on the vertical axis).*

e) **Use your graph** to draw a simple conclusion about the effect of temperature on the **RATE** of a chemical reaction.

f) Use your knowledge of the collision theory to **explain** your conclusion.

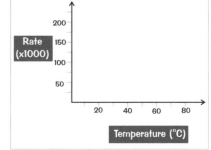

Q2 *The same reaction can be used to investigate the effect of CONCENTRATION on the rate of a reaction. In changing the concentration, it is important to keep the total volume used exactly the same.*

Volume of sodium thiosulphate (cm³)	50	40	30	20	10
Volume of water (cm³)	0				
Time taken (s)	80	101	137	162	191
Rate (1/t)					

a) **Complete** the table, adding the volume of water and calculating the rate of the reaction.

b) **Plot graphs** showing the time taken against volume of sodium thiosulphate used, and also rate against volume of sodium thiosulphate used.

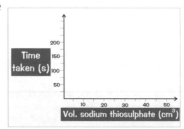 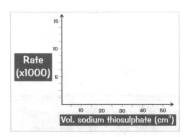

c) Use these graphs to draw a **simple conclusion** about the effect of concentration on the reaction rate.

d) **Explain** your conclusion in terms of particles and the collision theory.

Experiments on Rates of Reaction

Q3 *When magnesium reacts with acid, hydrogen gas is given off. This can be collected and measured as a way of measuring the rate of the reaction.*

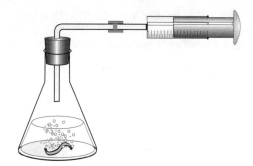

In this experiment 25cm³ of dilute hydrochloric acid (0.5mol/dm³) was reacted with a small amount of magnesium ribbon (the acid was in excess).

a) Write a **balanced equation** for this reaction. (*Mg + HCl → etc.*)

b) Use the results below to **plot a graph** of volume collected (vertical axis) against time (horizontal axis).

Time (s)	0	10	20	30	40	50	60	70	80	90	100
Vol. hydrogen (cm³)	0	9	18	27	36	44	50	54	56	57	57

c) **Mark** on your graph where the reaction is going at a constant rate.

d) **How much** hydrogen was collected in the first 25 seconds?

e) **How long** did it take to collect 40cm³ of hydrogen?

f) **Sketch** on the **same axis** the graphs you would expect if the experiment was repeated using 25cm³ of:

1.0 mol/dm³ acid .... mark this A.

2.0 mol/dm³ acid .... mark this B.

0.25 mol/dm³ acid .... mark this C.

Q4 *A similar experiment can be carried out to investigate the effect of changing the temperature on the rate of reaction. The graph below shows results from such an experiment. The acid is increasingly warmer in experiments 1, 2 and 3 .*

a) What **simple conclusion** can you draw from these graphs?

b) For each graph, **calculate** the rate over the first 10 seconds.

c) What do you notice about the **change in the rate** of the reaction for an increase of 10°C?

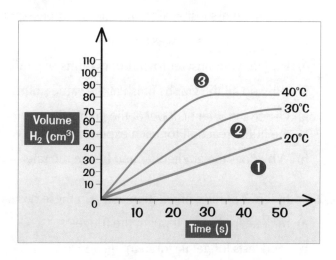

Top Tips:

Lots of graph-drawing practice here. Always make sure you've included a **title**, **axis labels** and **units** — and check the **scale's** about right. They'll look at all these in the Exam, and losing marks is so **easy**.

More on Rates of Reaction

Q1 *Marble chips react with acid to produce carbon dioxide gas. This loss of gas means that the reaction can be followed by recording the mass every 30 seconds on a balance.*

The experiment was repeated using different sized pieces of marble:

Experiment 1 .... large chips

Experiment 2 .... small chips

Experiment 3 .... powdered marble

a) In carrying out this experiment, **what factors** must be kept constant?

b) Use the results in the tables to **work out** the total mass lost after every 30 seconds.

Experiment 1

Time (s)	Mass (g)	Mass Lost (g)
0	100	0
30	99.8	
60	99.6	
90	99.4	
120	99.2	
150	99.0	
180	98.8	
210	98.6	
240	98.45	
270	98.30	
300	98.20	
330	98.15	
360	98.15	

Experiment 2

Time (s)	Mass (g)	Mass Lost (g)
0	100	0
30	99.7	
60	99.4	
90	99.1	
120	98.8	
150	98.6	
180	98.4	
210	98.3	
240	98.2	
270	98.15	
300	98.15	
330	98.15	
360	98.15	

Experiment 3

Time (s)	Mass (g)	Mass Lost (g)
0	100	0
30	99.0	
60	98.5	
90	98.3	
120	98.2	
150	98.15	
180	98.15	
210	98.15	
240	98.15	
270	98.15	
300	98.15	
330	98.15	
360	98.15	

c) **Plot** the mass lost against time for all three experiments on the same axes.

d) Which experiment was the **fastest**?

e) **Explain** your answer to part **d)** in terms of particles and collisions.

f) Why do all the graphs finish at the **same point**?

g) **Use the gradient** *(slope)* of the graphs in the first 60 seconds to **calculate** the rate of the initial reaction for each experiment *(mass lost ÷ time)*.

h) Why does the gradient — and hence the rate — **DECREASE** as the experiment goes on?

Q2 In terms of rates of reaction, **explain** these observations:

a) milk keeps longer if put in the fridge.

b) food lasts longer if stored in the freezer.

Q3 Give five everyday or industrial examples of each of these:

SLOW reactions (days or longer)	MODERATE reactions (hours / mins)	FAST reactions (seconds)

Catalysts

Q1 *The diagrams to the right show how 0.5g of zinc and 0.5g of copper react with dilute sulphuric acid.*

a) Does the **copper metal** react with dilute sulphuric acid?

b) Does **zinc** react with dilute sulphuric acid?

c) How do **zinc and copper** together react with dilute sulphuric acid?

d) **Describe** what copper does to the reaction in tube 3.

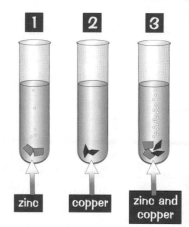

> **Tube 3 was left for several hours until the reaction was finished. The copper was removed, dried and weighed. Its mass was 0.5g.**

e) What does this tell you about the **action** of copper in speeding up the reaction between zinc and dilute sulphuric acid?

H Q2 *The graph shows an energy profile for a typical **exothermic** reaction.*

a) **Mark** on the graph:

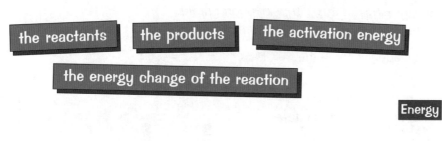

the reactants   the products   the activation energy

the energy change of the reaction

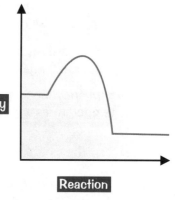

b) Use a different colour to mark the profile of the reaction when **catalysed**.

Q3 *Catalytic converters are found in almost every new car. Their function is to clean up exhaust emissions and stop pollution.*

a) Name **three** polluting gases found in "normal" car exhaust fumes.

b) Into what *"harmless gases"* are they converted?

"Even with the new catalytic converter, I can still smell smoke"

Catalysts

Q4 *The iron used in the manufacture of ammonia is often in the form of fine pellets.*
Why is the iron used in this form?

Q5 What are the **advantages** of using catalysts in the industrial manufacture of chemicals?

Q6 *The experiment shown can be used to investigate enzyme activity.*

Trypsin is an enzyme that catalyses the breakdown of protein. Photographic film has a protein layer that holds the silver compounds in place (these appear black). Different films use different proteins. If the protein is destroyed this black layer falls off leaving a clear plastic film.

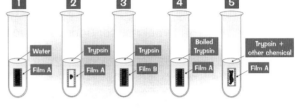

a) Look at the tubes carefully, then compare the pairs suggested, writing your **conclusion** in the table provided.

b) Why was **tube 1** included in the experiment?

Tubes	Possible conclusion
2 & 3	
2 & 4	
2 & 5	

Q7 *The ability of trypsin to break down protein depends on temperature.*
The experiment below investigates this. Strips of photographic film
were each left for ten minutes in test tubes at the temperatures shown.

a) From these results, what appears to be the **optimum temperature**?

b) Explain what happens to the enzyme at temperatures **above** the optimum temperature.

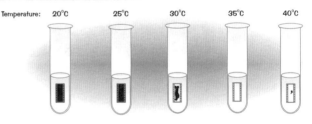

Q8 *The browning of apples after being cut is an enzyme-catalysed reaction.*
An apple was cut into slices and left in different conditions.

a) What **conclusion** can be drawn by comparing results 1 and 2?

b) What **conclusion** can be drawn from results 1 and 3?

c) What does **result 4** tell you about the nature of these catalysts?

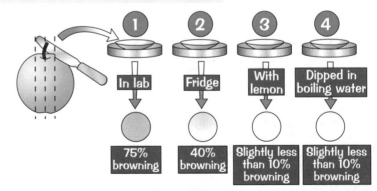

Top Tips:

The trickiest thing here is knowing how **activation energy** fits in — make sure you can **define** a **catalyst** in terms of it. Just don't forget how **specific** they are — and that they're **not used up** in reactions. Other than that, it's best to learn an **example** or two of how they're used in **industry** — a favourite Exam topic.

Enzymes

Q1   *Starch is converted to sugar by several enzymes:*

Which enzymes are the best at
converting starch to sugar?

Enzyme	Percentage conversion after 30 minutes
Pepsin	0
Amylase	87
Trypsin	0
Maltase	67
Sucrase	42

Q2   *Unfortunately the head teacher spilled custard down his clean white shirt. A group of
year 10 students offered to find the best way to get it clean. They cut up the shirt into
squares and tested each with a different wash to find the best way to remove the stain.*

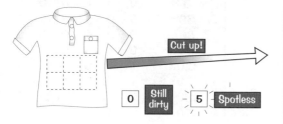

Treatment	How clean?
A) Hand wash in cold water	0
B) Warm wash with ordinary powder	3
C) 70°C wash with "Ace bio powder"	3
D) 40°C wash with "Ace bio powder"	5
E) Cold wash with "Ace bio powder"	3

a) Which wash gave the **best result**?

b) What is the special ingredient in "*bio*" or "*biological*" powders?

c) Why did tests C and E not give a spotless result?

Q3   *Cheese goes mouldy after a while.*

a) What causes cheese and other foods to go off?

b) Why does keeping cheese in the fridge help to
keep it fresh for longer?

c) **Explain** why meat or vegetables in the freezer
stay fresh for months.

Q4   *Loads of cream cakes were put in different places in the kitchen.*

In which order should they
be eaten if each is to be
enjoyed as a **FRESH** cake?

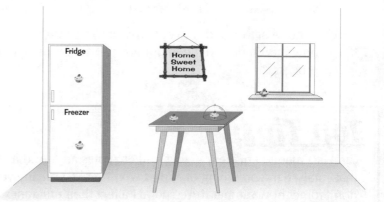

Enzymes

Q5 *The enzymes in yeast help to produce energy from sugar by breaking down glucose into carbon dioxide and ethanol.*

a) Write a **balanced equation** for this reaction.

The experiment was repeated at different temperatures and the volume of CO_2 recorded every 30 minutes. The results are shown in the table opposite:

b) Use the results to **plot eight graphs** on the same axes. Set the axes out as below.

(For easy comparison, use different colours for each temperature).

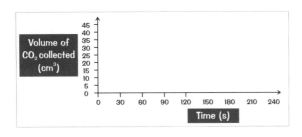

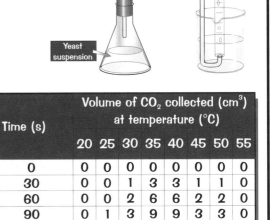

Time (s)	Volume of CO_2 collected (cm^3) at temperature (°C)							
	20	25	30	35	40	45	50	55
0	0	0	0	0	0	0	0	0
30	0	0	1	3	3	1	1	0
60	0	0	2	6	6	2	2	0
90	0	1	3	9	9	3	3	0
120	1	1	5	13	13	4	3	0
150	1	2	7	18	18	6	4	0
180	2	3	10	25	25	8	5	0
210	3	5	14	35	35	10	6	0
240	4	7	18	45	45	12	7	0

c) From your graphs, which temperature(s) appear to be the **best working temperature**(s) for this enzyme?

d) For each temperature, **calculate** the maximum rate of the fermentation (i.e. the steepest gradient).

e) Use these answers to **plot a graph** of rate against temperature, as shown on the right.

f) Use this graph to suggest the **optimum temperature** for this reaction.

g) **Explain** what happens to the enzyme at temperatures **above** this optimum temperature.

h) *The process of fermentation is very important.* **Name two** major products that depend on fermentation.

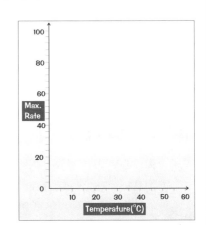

Q6 *Bacteria are used in the food industry as well as yeast.*

a) Milk is the starting material for which **two** major foods?

b) Why is **pasteurised milk** normally used instead of fresh milk?

c) For one of the foods in your answer to **a)**, **describe briefly** how it is made and the importance of the fermentation process.

Top Tips:

Simple Reversible Reactions

Q1   *Look at the two diagrams opposite.*

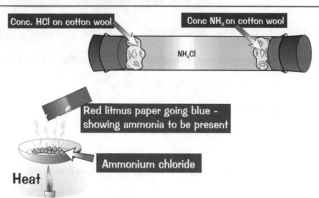

Conc. HCl on cotton wool

Conc NH₃ on cotton wool

NH₄Cl

Red litmus paper going blue - showing ammonia to be present

Ammonium chloride

Heat

a)   Write **balanced equations** for both the reactions in the diagrams.

b)   What does the **symbol** "⇌" mean?

c)   Use this symbol to rewrite your answer to part **a)** as a **single** equation.

H Q2   *Copper sulphate can be either blue crystals or a white powder.*

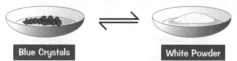

Blue Crystals   White Powder

a) How can you change the **blue crystals** to a **white powder**?

b) How can you **reverse** the process?

c) Write a fully **balanced equation** to describe this change.

H Q3   Study pictures A and B carefully.

a)   **Complete** the following passage using the words given in the box above the passage.

| equilibrium | open | up | down | dynamic | balanced |
| activity | change | static | closed | equilibrium | dynamic |

Picture **A** shows a see-saw which is perfectly _____ and not moving. It is in _____.
This type of _____ is said to be _____. Picture **B** shows a different type of
equilibrium. The escalator is moving _____, whilst the man is trying to walk _____.
There is constant _____, but no _____ in overall position. This is _____
equilibrium. All reversible reactions are examples of _____ equilibrium. Dynamic
equilibria always occur in _____ systems, where nothing can escape or get into the
system. An _____ system is like a jar with the lid off — things can escape.

Look at picture C — a full pop bottle.

b)   **What type** of equilibrium exists between the carbon dioxide dissolved in the drink and that in the air above it?

c)   What **type of system** does C represent?

d)   If the top were removed, what **type of system** would you have? What would happen to the equilibrium?

H Q4   *Look at the graph opposite.*

a)   What is happening to the reactants during **phase A**?

b)   What is happening at **point B**?

c)   What type of **equilibrium** is this?

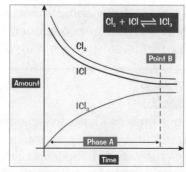

Cl₂ + ICl ⇌ ICl₃

Cl₂

Point B

ICl

Amount

ICl₃

Phase A

Time

Simple Reversible Reactions

H Q5   *Consider the reaction:* $N_2O_4{}_{(g)} \rightleftharpoons 2NO_2{}_{(g)}$ *ΔH is +ve (it's an endothermic reaction)*

Suggest what would happen to the equilibrium if you:

a) increased the **temperature**.

b) increased the **pressure**.

c) doubled the **concentration** of N_2O_4.

H Q6   The equation below shows the reaction occurring in the Haber process.

$N_2 + 3H_2 \rightleftharpoons 2NH_3$ *ΔH is -ve (it's an exothermic reaction)*

Suggest what would happen to the
position of equilibrium if you:

a) increased the **pressure**.

b) increased the **temperature**.

c) added more **nitrogen**.

d) removed the **ammonia**.

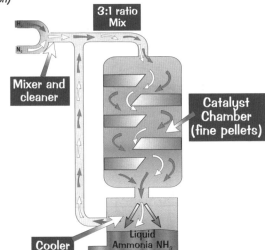

H Q7   *The diagram opposite shows the Haber Process.*

a) **Write** a fully balanced equation for the reaction,
including state symbols.

b) What **catalyst** is used?

c) What is the **function** of the catalyst?

d) Why are **fine pellets** used?

e) **Use the information** on these graphs to suggest the
optimum conditions for ammonia production.

f) **Explain** why high pressures are used.

g) *The actual conditions are often 450ºC and 200 atm
pressure.* **Explain** why these conditions are used.

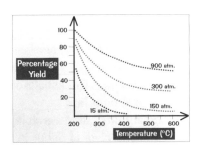

H Q8   *This reaction occurs in the Contact Process for making sulphuric acid:*

$2SO_2{}_{(g)} + O_2{}_{(g)} \rightleftharpoons 2SO_3{}_{(g)}$ *ΔH is -ve (it's exothermic)*

a) What is the effect on the position of equilibrium of increasing: (i) **temperature** (ii) **pressure**?

b) **Suggest** the optimum conditions that could be used for a high yield.

c) *The actual operating temperature is around 450ºC,
despite a poor yield (see graph).*
Explain why such a high temperature is used.

d) *In this process 100% conversion could be achieved using
extremely high pressures of around 1000 atm.* **Suggest** a
reason why this pressure is **not** used commercially.

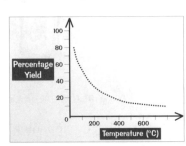

Top Tips:

If two things can **combine**, they can **separate** — **any** reaction's basically reversible. Usually though one
way's **much faster** than the other, so you don't notice. Make sure you understand **Le Chatelier's Principle**
— if you can picture what's happening at the **molecular** level, you're much more likely to **remember** it.

Energy Transfer in Reactions

Q1 **Fill in the blanks** in the following passage (the words can be used more than once):

energy	exothermic	endothermic	cold	taken in	
hot	given out	negative	ΔH	energy	break	made

A reaction that gives out _____ is called an _____
reaction. A reaction that takes in _____ is called an
_____ reaction. _____ reactions can feel _____ as
energy is_____ _____. _____ reactions can feel _____ as
energy is _____ ____. The energy change of a reaction is often given
the symbol _____. For _____ reactions the energy change is
positive, i.e. heat is needed. A _____ energy change indicates an
exothermic reaction, i.e. heat is released.
Virtually all chemical reactions involve _____ changes. Whether
they are _____ or _____ depends on the balance between
the _____ needed to _____ bonds in the reactant, and the
_____released when bonds are_____ in the products.

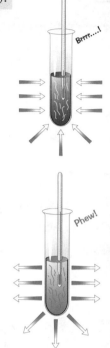

Q2 **Classify these reactions** or changes as exothermic or endothermic:

a) Burning a fuel.

b) Neutralising an acid.

c) Thermal decomposition of copper carbonate.

d) Rapid oxidation of iron.

e) Rapid dissolving of ammonium nitrate.

f)

g)

H Q3 Here are some more bond energies (kJ/mol): N≡N = 945, H-H = 435, N-H = 389

a) How much energy is needed to **break** the N≡N bond?

b) How much energy is needed to **break** the H-H bond?

c) How much energy is **released** when the N-H bonds are formed?

d) Write out the equation below using **structural** formulae for the molecules.

$$N_{2(g)} + 3H_{2(g)} \rightleftharpoons 2NH_{3(g)}$$

e) **Calculate** the energy needed to break all the reactant bonds.

f) Work out the **energy released** when the products are formed.

g) Hence calculate the **overall energy change** (i.e. **the net energy transfer**) for the reaction and **state** whether it is an **exothermic** or **endothermic** reaction.

Energy Transfer in Reactions

H Q4 *Burning ethanol can be represented by the following equation:*

$$C_2H_5OH + 3O_2 \rightarrow 2CO_2 + 3H_2O$$

Bond energies (kJ/mol): C-C = 346, C-H = 413, C=O = 740,

C-O = 360, O-H = 463, O=O = 497.

a) Write out the equation using **structural** formulae for the molecules.

b) **Calculate** the energy needed to break all the reactant bonds.

c) **Work out** the energy released when all the product bonds are formed.

d) **Calculate** the overall energy change, ΔH, and state clearly whether it is **positive** or **negative**.

e) **State** whether the reaction is **exothermic** or **endothermic**.

H Q5 Consider the reaction:

$$CH_4 + 2O_2 \rightarrow CO_2 + 2H_2O$$

Bond energies (kJ/mol): C-H = 413, O=O = 497, C=O = 740, O-H = 463

Given the above bond energies, **calculate:**

a) the total energy needed to **break all** of the bonds of the reactants.

b) the total energy **released** in making the bonds of the products.

c) the total **energy change** (i.e. the **net energy transfer**) for this reaction.

d) Mark on the energy profile →

  i) The reactants ($CH_4 + 2O_2$).

  ii) The products ($CO_2 + 2H_2O$).

  iii) ΔH.

  iv) The activation energy.

e) Is this an **exothermic** or

  endothermic reaction?

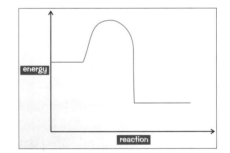

H Q6 *In the **Contact Process** for making sulphuric acid, sulphur dioxide is catalytically converted to sulphur trioxide:*

a) **Mark** on the profile:

  i) The reactants.

  ii) The products.

  iii) ΔH.

  iv) The activation energy.

b) **Mark** on the diagram the profile you would expect for a reaction catalysed by vanadium(V) oxide.

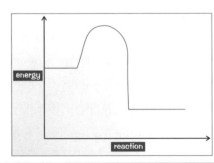

$$2SO_{2\,(g)} + O_{2\,(g)} \rightleftharpoons 2SO_3$$

Top Tips:

This sort of thing's difficult at first — but once it's **clicked**, you'll remember it. Just don't forget that pulling things apart **takes energy** — so **breaking** bonds is **endothermic**, while **making** them is **exothermic**. Just make sure you can calculate the total energy **change** of a reaction (**ΔH**) from **bond energies**.

These are for checking, NOT COPYING, be warned.

ANSWERS

Materials and Their Properties

We've included the answers to the ODD numbered questions. That way...

- Teach can set questions that you can check yourself.
- Teach can set questions that you can't cheat on (not that you would).
- You can use the questions for practice when you're revising — and check you know your stuff.

If you need the rest of the answers, take a look at the 'AQA — Materials and Their Properties' answer book.

Pages 1, 2

1) Solid, liquid, gas

3)

| Solid | Liquid | Gas |

5) **a)** Solids, strongest forces of attraction.

b) Gases have the weakest forces of attraction. Particles are widely spaced out hence few in a certain volume (i.e. they have the lowest density)

c) Gas, all particles are in rapid and random motion.

d) Solid, liquid and gas respectively. Ice, water and steam respectively.

e) Particles are already packed closely together. Car brakes make use of this — any sensible answer.

f) It's quite large compared with the distance between particles in a liquid.

g) By particles bouncing off the sides of the container.

h) The pressure would increase. The molecules are given more energy, so move more quickly and collide with the container walls harder and more often.

7) A = melting, B = boiling/evaporating, C = condensing, D = freezing/solidifying

9) **a)** 25°C

b) Oxygen

c) Zinc

d) Bromine or Mercury

e) Oxygen

f) Mercury

g) Zinc

h) Bromine

i) The heat energy goes to the molecules which makes them vibrate more and more. Eventually the bonds between the molecules are overcome and the molecules start to move around. It has now melted.

j) When a liquid is heated the heat energy goes to the molecules. This makes the molecules move faster. Some molecules move faster than others. Fast moving molecules at the surface will overcome the forces of attraction from the other molecules and escape. This is evaporation. It is a form of heat transfer.

11) Particles join up (bond) together and move around less. Particles become regularly arranged and vibrate about a fixed position.

Page 3

1) A   3) C

5) B or D   7) D

9) See table:

Name	Molecular formula	Structural formula	Molecular model
Water	H_2O	H—O—H	
Ammonia	NH_3	H—N—H (H)	
Ethane	C_2H_6	H—C—C—H (H H / H H)	
Carbon dioxide	CO_2	O=C=O	

Page 4

1) **a)** Smallest particle of an element with the properties of that element. The basic building block of all matter.

b) 3 main particles.

c) Protons, neutrons and electrons.

d) Small structure consisting of protons and neutrons at the centre of the atom making up almost all the mass.

e) A group of electrons with the same energy.

3)

Particle	Mass	Charge	Where it is found
Proton	1	+1	In the nucleus
Electron	$\frac{1}{1836}$	-1	Orbiting the nucleus
Neutron	1	0	In the nucleus

5) a million (1×10^6)

7) 7

9) **a)** p+ = 6,   e- = 6, n^0 = 6.

b) p+ = 19,   e- = 19, n^0 = 20.

c) p+ = 1,   e- = 1, n^0 = 0.

11) **a)** protons = 1, electrons = 1, neutrons = 1

b) protons = 1, electrons = 1, neutrons = 2

Pages 5, 6

1) The electrons orbit around the nucleus with the nucleus taking the part of the sun, and the electrons playing the role of the planets.

3) Shell

5)

Element	Symbol	Atomic Number	Mass Number	Number of Protons	Number of Electrons	Number of Neutrons	Electronic Configuration	Group Number
Hydrogen	H	1	1	1	1	0	1	—
Helium	He	2	4	2	2	2	2	0
Lithium	Li	3	7	3	3	4	2, 1	1
Beryllium	Be	4	9	4	4	5	2, 2	2
Boron	B	5	11	5	5	6	2, 3	3
Carbon	C	6	12	6	6	6	2, 4	4
Nitrogen	N	7	14	7	7	7	2, 5	5
Oxygen	O	8	16	8	8	8	2, 6	6
Fluorine	F	9	19	9	9	10	2, 7	7
Neon	Ne	10	20	10	10	10	2, 8	0
Sodium	Na	11	23	11	11	12	2, 8, 1	1
Magnesium	Mg	12	24	12	12	12	2, 8, 2	2
Aluminium	Al	13	27	13	13	14	2, 8, 3	3
Silicon	Si	14	28	14	14	14	2, 8, 4	4
Phosphorus	P	15	31	15	15	16	2, 8, 5	5
Sulphur	S	16	32	16	16	16	2, 8, 6	6
Chlorine	Cl	17	35	17	17	18	2, 8, 7	7
Argon	Ar	18	40	18	18	22	2, 8, 8	0
Potassium	K	19	39	19	19	20	2, 8, 8, 1	1
Calcium	Ca	20	40	20	20	20	2, 8, 8, 2	2

7) All noble gases have a full outer shell / Every element with a full outer shell in its atoms is a noble gas.

9) 4

11) Reactivity.

13)

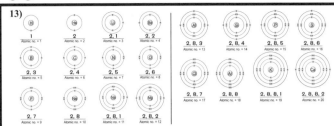

Page 7

1)

Substance	Element	Mixture	Compound
Copper	✓		
Air		✓	
Distilled water			✓
Brine		✓	
Sodium	✓		
Cupro-nickel		✓	
Sodium chloride			✓
Copper sulphate			✓
Sulphur	✓		
Oxygen	✓		
Sea water		✓	
Bronze		✓	
Petrol		✓	
Blue Ink		✓	
Steel		✓	
Steam			✓
Milk		✓	

3) Compounds consist of different elements chemically combined in fixed proportions.

5) A mixture is a collection of different elements and/or compounds combined in variable proportions. They can be separated by physical means.

Pages 8, 9

1) An atom or molecule that is charged because it has gained or lost electrons.

3) NH_4^+, CO_3^{2-} or any other sensible example.

5)

7) positive

9) The electrostatic attraction between oppositely charged ions formed by losing or gaining electrons.

11) 1+

13) As they have gained an electron and thus have one more electron than protons (only needed to gain one electron to have a full outer shell).

15) 2–

17) A cation is a positively charged ion and an anion is a negatively charged ion.

19)   **21)**

23) a) Sodium d) Nitrate g) Fluoride j) Magnesium
   b) Chloride e) Sulphate h) Potassium k) Phosphate
   c) Sulphide f) Iodide i) Calcium l) Hydrogen
          m) Barium

25) a, b

Pages 10, 11

1) A number of atoms joined together by covalent bonds.

3) One or more pairs of electrons.

5) So they have a more stable, full outer shell of electrons.

7) 2, 8   **9)** 1 more
    11) a, d, e

13)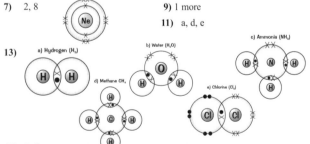

15) 2, 6

17) Neon

19)

Page 12

1) a) / b)
Element → Metal → "giant metallic" → e.g. Mg, Zn, Ca, Cu.

Element → Non-metal → "molecular" → e.g. O_2, I_2, S_8, P_5.

Element → Non-metal → "giant" → e.g. C.

Mixture → Metal/metal alloy → "giant" → e.g. bronze, cupronickel

Compound → Metal/non-metal → "ions, giant" → e.g. NaCl, $CuSO_4$, KI, KCl.

Compound → Non-metal → "molecular" → e.g. SO_2, PCl_3, CO_2, HCl, C_2H_4.

Compound → Non-metal → "giant" → SiO_2.

3) Because applying a force to them (e.g. hitting a crystal with a hammer) will disrupt the ionic lattice and bring together like charges which repel, thus the crystal lattice will split.

5) Giant structures, e.g. silicon dioxide (sand), diamond.

7) The water molecules split apart the ionic lattice (because of their dipole) and surround the separated ions, holding them in solution.

Page 13

1) The atoms are held together by free moving electrons which fix the metal ions into a regular arrangement.

3) They are electrons from metal atoms in the lattice originating from the outer shells of electrons of each metal.

5) a)

Metal Property	Good Example	Reason	Exception
Strong	Iron*	strong bonds	Mercury*
Good Conductor of Heat	Any metal	free moving electrons	none
Good Conductor of electricity	Gold*	free moving electrons	none
Can be rolled into sheets (malleable)	Aluminium*	atoms can slide over each other	Mercury*
Can be drawn into wires (ductile)	Copper*	atoms can slide over each other	Mercury*

b) A metallic bond.   * or any other suitable example

7) They provide different properties from the constituent metals.

9) a) H; very high melting point

b) F; low melting point / good electrical conductor and unreactive.

c) A; low density, doesn't react with water (in rain clouds).

d) E; high specific heat capacity, low m.p. so can be used as a liquid.

e) A; low density, fairly high electrical conductivity

Page 14

1)

 Oxidising
Example: liquid oxygen

Harmful
Example: methanol

Highly flammable
Example: petrol

Corrosive
Example: sulphuric acid

Toxic
Example: cyanide

Irritant
Example: bleach

Radioactive
Example: uranium

Explosive
Example: hydrogen

3) Using extreme care/ at least eye protection/wipe up spills/ industrial fully protective clothing might be used.

Page 15

1) Plants and animals died and were covered over by sediment in the sea. After millions of years of pressure and heat, these remains became crude oil.

3) Different sized hydrocarbon molecules.

5) Because it is a mixture of lots of different hydrocarbons.

7) It is piped, or transported in tankers.

9) Oil spills can harm marine life such as fish and birds and damage beaches.

11) Advantages - 1) Produces lots of energy for the cost. 2) Available in liquid form which is light - easy to transport. 3) The main products (CO_2, H_2O) are non toxic. Disadvantages - 1) Produces CO_2 which causes the greenhouse effect. 2) They are non-renewable. 3) Minor products are toxic or highly damaging to environment (CO, SO2, Pb products form leaded petrol).

Page 16

1) A fuel formed from the fossilised remains of plants and/or animals.

3) a) Vaporises easily

b) Sets on fire easily

c) Purifying

d) Turns from a liquid to a gas

e) Different components of a mixture, which have been separated from the mixture by distillation.

f) A process of separation, involving heating a mixture of liquids until it vaporizes, then cooling it to condense the vapour and collecting the resultant liquid

g) Thick liquid.

h) Gases such as butane or propane which can be used as bottled gas.

Answers

i) A series of covalently bonded carbon atoms as found in molecules such as hydrocarbons.

5) Fractional distillation splits crude oil up into its different fractions (the different hydrocarbons it contains). Each fraction has a different boiling point. The fractionating column goes from being really hot at the bottom to being cooler at the top, arranged so each different fraction can be condensed and tapped off at the place in the column which is the same temperature as that fraction's boiling point.

7) As the length increases, flammability decreases.

9) Short.

11) There is a limited amount, i.e. oil will eventually run out.

13) Try to prevent oil spillages; promote public transport (more efficient use of petrol); invest in renewable energy resources e.g. solar power, wind power; more legislation and education.

Pages 17, 18

1)
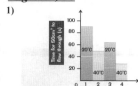

3) Ace oil.

5) Do the experiment at the average temperature of a car engine.

7) It might solidify or become too viscous.

9) Breaking complicated molecules down into simpler molecules by heating them.

11) a) Heat, a catalyst.

b) An alkene is a hydrocarbon molecule with a C=C double bond.

c) They have double or triple bonds, which means other chemicals will react easily with them.

d) Paraffin is saturated, and so cannot react with the bromine water.

The gas A is an alkene, it is unsaturated and so it reacts with the bromine water and decolourises it.

e)
$$H \quad\quad H$$
$$C = C$$
$$H \quad\quad H$$

f) Ethene.

13) a) Cracking (thermal decomposition)

b) C_2H_4 , C_6H_{12}

c) $C_{16}H_{34}$, C_6H_{14}

d) i) C_2H_4 , C_6H_{12} ii) C_2H_4 , C_6H_{12}

e) To prevent the alkene produced reacting with the air.

f)
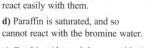

g) Making plastics, and other chemicals e.g. petrol additives.

h) A polymer - poly(ethene).

i) Poly(vinylchloride) or poly(chloroethene) – PVC.

Pages 19, 20

1)

Name	Formula	Number of Carbons	Melting Point(°C)	Boiling Point(°C)	Structural (graphical) Formula
Methane	CH_4	1	-182	-164	H-C-H
Ethane	C_2H_6	2	-183	-89	H-C-C-H
Propane	C_3H_8	3	-190	-42	H-C-C-C-H
Butane	C_4H_{10}	4	-138	0	H-C-C-C-C-H
Pentane	C_5H_{12}	5	-130	36	H-C-C-C-C-C-H
Hexane	C_6H_{14}	6	-95	69	H-C-C-C-C-C-C-H
Heptane	C_7H_{16}	7	-91	99	H-C-C-C-C-C-C-C-H
Octane	C_8H_{18}	8	-57	126	H-C-C-C-C-C-C-C-C-H
Nonane	C_9H_{20}	9	-51	151	H-C-C-C-C-C-C-C-C-C-H
Decane	$C_{10}H_{22}$	10	-30	174	H-C-C-C-C-C-C-C-C-C-C-H

3) a) None listed;

b) Pentane, hexane, heptane, octane, nonane, decane

c) Butane, propane, ethane, methane.

5) Because, if the chains are heavier and longer, they need more heat to break free from each other.

7) See diagram:

9) That the molecule contains no double or triple bonds.

11) i) methane + oxygen → carbon dioxide + water
$$CH_4 + 2O_2 \rightarrow CO_2 + 2H_2O$$
ii) ethane + oxygen → carbon dioxide + water
$$2C_2H_6 + 7O_2 \rightarrow 4CO_2 + 6H_2O$$
iii) propane + oxygen → carbon dioxide + water
$$C_3H_8 + 5O_2 \rightarrow 3CO_2 + 4H_2O$$

13) Alkanes are saturated, they have no spare electrons available to bond and this makes them unreactive, e.g. ethane.

15) Alkanes are more valuable — many products can be made from them.

17) For safety reasons it is given a smell so that a leak can be noticed.

CH_4 C_2H_6

C_3H_8

C_4H_{10}

C_6H_{12}

Pages 21, 22

1) a) They have a double or triple bond and so have spare electrons available to bond.

b) They can react with other chemicals, and polymerise.

3) a) There are twice as many hydrogen atoms in each alkene molecule as there are carbon atoms.

b) i) C_2H_4.

ii)

or an isomer.

5) a)

b) This molecule has a C=C double bond. Ethane has no double bonds. Less hydrogen atoms.

7) a) i) The ethene will decolourise the bromine water to form a clear solution.

ii) Nothing happens as ethane cannot react with the bromine water because it is saturated.

9) a) A single repeated unit of a polymer.

b) Polymerisation.

11) a) butene + oxygen → carbon dioxide + water

b) butene + chlorine → dichlorobutane

c) butene + bromine → dibromobutane

d) propene + oxygen → carbon dioxide + water

(Detailed naming of organic compounds not required)

Pages 23, 24

1) Lots of small units join up to make a long chain.

3) a) Poly(ethene) — polythene.

b)

c) Poly(ethene) - because it is made up of lots of molecules of ethene.

d) Because ethene can undergo substitution reactions, so different groups can be added to the ethene monomers, giving the polymers they form (the plastics) different properties.

5) Polymerisation; Carbon; Addition; Monomer; Polymer; Plastics; Polythene; Monomer ethene; Ethene monomers; High pressure; Catalyst; Double bond; Saturated.

7)

Good points	Bad points
Fairly Cheap	Can catch fire
Low density	Difficult to dispose of
Moulded easily (can be made into desired shape easily)	Non-degradable
	May produce toxic gases when burnt
Can be made very strong	Moulded easily (may be
Can be coloured	unintentionally deformed).
Not affected by acids or alkalis	
Insulators	

Page 25

1) A mineral containing enough metal to make it worth extracting from the ground.

3) As pure metal.

5) As compounds (metal ores).

7) Electrolysis of Molten Ore

potassium   aluminium   calcium

sodium   magnesium

Reduction of Ore With Carbon

zinc   iron   lead

Thermal Decomposition of Ore

copper

Occurs Naturally

silver   gold   (copper, iron) — v.rare

Page 26

1) a) Because iron is lower in the reactivity series than carbon, so can be reduced by it. Sodium and aluminium are above carbon in the reactivity series.

b) haematite   c) oxygen   d) Fe_2O_3

3) a) By the coke burning.   b) $C + O_2 \rightarrow CO_2$

5) a) $3CO + Fe_2O_3 \rightarrow 3CO_2 + 2Fe$ b) it has been reduced.   c) $Fe^{3+} + 3e^- \rightarrow Fe$

d) i) Liquid   ii) It runs to the bottom of the furnace where it is tapped off.

7) Some other metals are extracted by electrolysis which is expensive because it uses a lot of electricity. Burning coke is far cheaper.

9) Making steel, nails, tools, blades, electromagnets.

98

Page 27

1)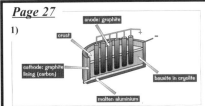

7) **a)** Cathode

b) Anode.

9) oxygen + carbon › carbon dioxidc

3) Because the impurities might be electrolysed instead of the aluminium.

5) Lowering the melting point brings the required temperature down to about 900 °C, which is cheaper and safer.

Page 28

1) –ve cathode; +ve anode.

3) Electrons.

5) $Cu \rightarrow Cu^{2+} + 2e^-$

7) Because it's less reactive.

9) Gas and water pipes, non-corroding alloys like brass and bronze; covering domes on mosques, cooking pans.

11) Transition metals

13) High melting point good thermal conductivity.

15) No. It is more dense than water.

Pages 29, 30

1) **a)** Yes

b) Ceramic

c) No

d) Titanium or ceramic

e) Preferably

f) Mild steel or ceramic

g) Yes

h) Ceramic

i) No

j) Ceramic

k) Titanium. Titanium is strong and hard, with a low reactivity although it is very dense and very expensive. Mild steel is strong, hard and cheap but has a high reactivity and a high density. Ceramic is strong, hard, cheap, has a low reactivity and a low density but it is brittle.

3)

Property (Quality)	Give two examples	Give an exception to this rule	Why is this quality of use?
Metals are solid	Any except mercury	mercury	Construction of buildings
Metals are strong (have high tensile strength)	aluminium titanium	mercury	Construction
Metals are shiny	most	lead	Jewellery, foil
Metals bend	most	mercury	Shaping them
Metals are tough (hard wearing)	titanium copper	sodium	Bearings
Metals usually feel cold (conduct heat)	copper silver	lead	Heat exchangers
Metals conduct electricity well	copper aluminium	lead	Cables, wires
Metals are dense (heavy for their size)	lead gold	lithium	Sea anchors
Some metals are magnetic (repel magnetic poles)	iron nickel	all except iron, nickel, cobalt	Magnets, speakers
Metals are sonorous (make a nice noise when struck)	copper tin	mercury	Musical instruments
Metals expand when heating	lead mercury	tungsten	Thermometers Bimetallic strips
Metals react with the oxygen in the air	Most	gold, platinum	Protective layers (eg aluminium oxide)
Metals react with acids	All above H in R.Series	gold, silver	Batteries, manufacture of salts

Pages 31, 32

1) It produces ammonia, which is needed to make fertilisers, explosives and plastics.

3) **a)** To give a large surface area for the reactants to be in contact.

b) Speeds it up

c) Turns ammonia gas into a liquid to be decanted off.

d) These conditions favour the reaction, making ammonia.

e) Molecules collide with less energy — less effective collisions and this would slow the rate of reaction.

f) i) $N_2 + 3H_2 \rightleftharpoons 2NH_3$
ii) equilibrium or reversible reaction

g) Despite the catalyst and favourable conditions the equilibrium still leaves much of the raw materials unreacted. This is compensated by recycling these gases for another pass around the chamber.

5) Ammonia; Haber Process; fertilisers; nitrogen; hydrogen; 450; pressure; 200; unreacted; recycled; atoms, hydrogen; atom; nitrogen.

7) **a)** Gives out heat

b) Increases the yield by moving the reaction equilibrium to the right hand side.

c) Since the forward reaction is exothermic, increasing the temperature will stimulate the reverse reaction to try to remove this excess heat. So the yield is lowered, but the rate is increased (poor yield produced fast).

d) At higher temperature the rate of reaction is greater. The lower yield is more than compensated by the much greater reaction rate.

e) Higher pressure brings the reactants closer together so the molecules collide much more frequently and react more often. The yield is increased because the forward reaction, which tries to reduce the pressure, is favoured. Thus increased pressure increases the yield.

f) Without the catalyst the rate is far too slow. Also enables reaction to take place at a lower temperature.

Page 33

1) Calcium carbonate.

3) Chalk, marble.

5) Remains of sea creatures which formed layers on the sea bottom.

7) Cheap and easily available.

9) Cement.

11) It fixes bricks together.

13) Plants sensitive to changes in pH. Most prefer neutral or slightly alkaline soil.

15) Base.

17) Acid rain attacks the limestone in buildings and statues, dissolving them.

Page 34

1) Reduction is the loss of oxygen. Oxidation is the gain of oxygen.

3) Reduction is the gain of electrons. Oxidation is the loss of electrons.

Pages 35, 36

1) **a)** iron sulphide

b) iron oxide

c) magnesium oxide

d) sulphur dioxide

e) water

f) magnesium sulphide

g) aluminium chloride

h) hydrogen iodide

i) carbon dioxide

j) iron bromide

k) potassium chloride

l) iron sulphide

m) lead oxide

n) calcium oxide

3) **a)** $C + O_2 \rightarrow CO_2$

b) $Zn + H_2SO_4 \rightarrow ZnSO_4 + H_2$

c) $Cu + 2Cl \rightarrow CuCl_2$

d) $H_2 + CuO \rightarrow Cu + H_2O$

e) $Mg + H_2SO_4 \rightarrow MgSO_4 + H_2$

f) $Mg + CuSO_4 \rightarrow Cu + MgSO_4$

g) $CuCO_3 \rightarrow CuO + CO_2$

h) $KOH + HCl \rightarrow KCl + H_2O$

i) $NaOH + HCl \rightarrow NaCl + H_2O$

j) $CaCO_3 + H_2SO_4 \rightarrow CaSO_4 + H_2O + CO_2$

5) **a)** $CaCO_3 \rightarrow CaO + CO_2$

b) $MgO + 2HCl \rightarrow MgCl_2 + H_2O$

c) $2SO_2 + O_2 \rightarrow 2SO_3$

d) $Na_2CO_3 + 2HNO_3 \rightarrow 2NaNO_3 + H_2O + CO_2$

e) $N_2 + 3H_2 \rightarrow 2NH_3$

Page 37

1) **a)** $N_2 + 3H_2 \rightarrow 2NH_3$

b) $CaCO_3 + H_2SO_4 \rightarrow CaSO_4 + H_2O + CO_2$

c) $2H_2 + O_2 \rightarrow 2H_2O$

d) $2Mg + O_2 \rightarrow 2MgO$

e) $2Ca + O_2 \rightarrow 2CaO$

f) $H_2 + I_2 \rightarrow 2HI$

g) $Mg + H_2SO_4 \rightarrow MgSO_4 + H_2$

h) $H_2SO_4 + 2NaOH \rightarrow Na_2SO_4 + 2H_2O$

i) $Ca + H_2SO_4 \rightarrow CaSO_4 + H_2$

j) $H_2SO_4 + 2KOH \rightarrow K_2SO_4 + 2H_2O$

k) $2HCl + MgO \rightarrow MgCl_2 + H_2O$

l) $CH_4 + 2O_2 \rightarrow CO_2 + 2H_2O$

m) $2H_2 + 2NO \rightarrow 2H_2O + N_2$

n) $2HCl + Ca(OH)_2 \rightarrow CaCl_2 + 2H_2O$

o) $Fe_2O_3 + 3CO \rightarrow 2Fe + 3CO_2$

p) $C_6H_{12}O_6 + 6O_2 \rightarrow 6CO_2 + 6H_2O$

q) $6CO_2 + 6H_2O \rightarrow C_6H_{12}O_6 + 6O_2$

r) $2C_4H_{10} + 13O_2 \rightarrow 8CO_2 + 10H_2O$

s) $C_2H_4 + 3O_2 \rightarrow 2CO_2 + 2H_2O$

t) $C_3H_8 + 5O_2 \rightarrow 3CO_2 + 4H_2O$

u) $C_5H_{12} + 8O_2 \rightarrow 5CO_2 + 6H_2O$

v) $2C_3H_6 + 9O_2 \rightarrow 6CO_2 + 6H_2O$

w) $2C_2H_6 + 7O_2 \rightarrow 4CO_2 + 6H_2O$

Page 38

Elements

1) 40

3) 56

5) 14

7) 1

9) 39

11) 80

13) 48

15) 197

17) 184

19) 201

Molecules: 21) 2   23) 71   25) 160   27) 38

(Note: no gram symbols)

Page 39

Compounds

1) 80

3) 166

5) 36.5

7) 119

9) 103

11) 160

13) 18

15) 17

17) 28

19) 133.5

21) 64

23) 136

25) 233

27) 461

29) 102

31) 100

33) 78

35) 158

37) 154

39) 60

41) 35

43) 132

45) 74

47) 188

49) 164

Page 40

1) 27.27%

3) 52.35%

5) 80%

7) 50%

9) 60%

11) 82.35%

13) 36%

15) 51.61%

17) 38.61%

19) 35%

21) **a)** M_r of CH_4 = 16 % carbon = $\frac{12}{16}$ x 100 = 75%

Answers

b) M_r of C_6H_6 = 78 % carbon = $\frac{72}{78}$ x 100 = 92.31%

c) M_r of C_2H_5OH = 46 % carbon = $\frac{24}{46}$ x 100 = 52.17%

C_6H_6 has the greatest proportion of carbon.

23) c) magnetite (Fe_3O_4)

25) 0.33%

Pages 41, 42

1) CH_3

3) CO_2

5) CaF_2

7) Na_3AlF_6

9) KNO_3

11) $AlCl_3$

13) sulphur trioxide — ratio of sulphur to oxygen in the compound is 1:3.

15) $PbCl_2$

17) $Ca(OH)_2$ — calcium hydroxide

Pages 43, 44

1) 8.8g

3) 5.6g

5) 8.8g

7) 12.4g

9) 112 tonnes

11) 230g of sodium

13) 280g

15) a) 1,889g (1.889kg)

b) 3,778g (3.778kg)

c) 8,500g (8.5kg)

d) 1,889kg (1.889 tonnes)

17) 24g

19) 23.28kg

Page 45

1) a) 192 litres
b) 2.4 litres
c) 2.4 litres
d) 476 cm³
e) 2400 cm³
f) 2400 cm³

3) a) 4 g
b) 0.5 g
c) 24 g
d) 4 g
e) 0.25 g

5) a) 0.2 g
b) 2400 cm³
c) 4 g
d) 48 000 cm³
e) 1.2 g

Page 47

1) a) anode

b) cathode

c) chlorine ion with a 1- charge; sodium ion with a 1+ charge; solid sodium chloride compound; chlorine gas.

3) a) electrons; ions; 23g

b) i) 1 mole **ii)** 24,000cm³

Page 48

1) As rain falls through the air some carbon dioxide dissolves in it, which forms carbonic acid.

3) A fuel formed from the fossilised remains of dead plants and/or animals.

5) Burning.

7) Sulphuric acid, nitric acid.

9) a) Coal

b) Clean the waste gases they produce, to remove the acidic oxides before releasing them into the atmosphere.

11) Limestone

Page 49

1) The Sun's light (visible) passes through the glass into the greenhouse and is absorbed by plants and soil. But IR rays emitted by plants and soil (low freq.) are reflected from the glass, so the greenhouse gets warmer.

3)

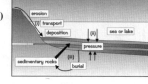

5) a)

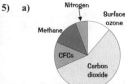

b) carbon dioxide.

c) burning fossil fuels, chopping down trees (which use up carbon dioxide).

Page 50

1) a) 42cm³

b) 21%

c) oxygen

d) it has reacted with the copper to form copper oxide

e) copper + oxygen → copper oxide

f) to allow the air in the syringe to return to room temperature,

as it was at the beginning of the experiment — a fair comparison of the volume of air in the syringe can then be made.

g) Carbon dioxide: fire extinguishers, nitrogen: inert atmospheres, noble gases: lighting/lasers etc.

Page 51

1) No. Little oxygen and too many toxic gases like sulphur dioxide/ammonia and methane.

3) The green plants, which undergo photosynthesis.

5) A drop in the temperature of the Earth caused water to condense to form the oceans.

7) Nitrates provide nutrients for plants growth. Removing the ammonia produces a better habitat for plant development.

9) glucose + oxygen → carbon dioxide + water

11) CO_2 levels will increase and this could add to the greenhouse effect and cause global warming.

Pages 52, 53

1) a) A - weathering,
B - transportation,
C - deposition,
E - burial and compression,
F - metamorphic rocks,
G - melting,
H - igneous rocks.

b) Heat and pressure causes crushing of rocks, and recrystallization may occur, forming metamorphic rocks.

c) Crystal structure of sedimentary rocks can change without melting.

d) Freeze thaw, biological (trees etc.), wind, waves, acid rain, rivers.

3)

Description	Meaning	Associated with forming:
a) Deposition	Rock deposited in different areas after weathering transport	Sedimentary rock
b) Burial	Rock buried under other rock	Sedimentary rock + metamorphic rock
c) Melting	Heat causes rock to melt	Igneous rock
d) Compression	Sediment compressed by weight of rock on top	Sedimentary rock
e) Recrystallization	Rock heated under pressure	Metamorphic rock

5) Has changed in form or structure.

7)

Sedimentary rock	Metamorphic
a) Limestone	Marble
b) Mudstone	Slate
c) Sandstone	Quartzite

9) Crystals that form igneous rocks are irregularly shaped and keyed into each other. Sedimentary rocks contain rounded crystals that are held together with weak, salt based cement.

11) Sediment.

Page 54

1)

a) Marble	Metamorphic
b) Schist	Metamorphic
c) Shale	Sedimentary
d) Slate	Metamorphic
e) Sandstone	Sedimentary
f) Granite	Igneous

3) a) Intrusive, large, magma.

b) Extrusive, small. Erupts, volcano.

Pages 55, 56

1) a) Water squeezed out and cement formed.

b) Salts from sea/rock form cement.

c) They melt or change in some way destroying the fossil remains.

d)

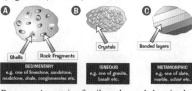

e) Oil.

3) a) (iv). **b)** (i). **c)** (ii). **d)** (iii).

5) a) i) D. **ii)** C.

b) E.

c) i) A. **ii)** D (assuming E is soil)

d) It was under water at some point.

e) Igneous (intrusive).

7)

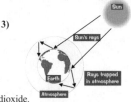

Reasons: A contains fossils and rounded grains held together by salt based cement. B contains randomly orientated interlocking crystals C is banded — all typical of that rock type.
Examples: A — sandstone, B — granite, C — marble.

Page 57

1) Earth movements e.g. earthquakes, continental drift; tilting, tipping from these major movements. Or weight of sediment above.

3) a) Marble.
b) Slate.
c) Schist.

5) Minerals from deep in the Earth are brought to the surface in magma.

Page 58

1) **a)** More gently heated more control goes no higher than 100°C

b) i) Plunge tube into ice **ii)** Leave to cool in water bath after turning off Bunsen.

c) slow cooling.

3) **a) – d)**
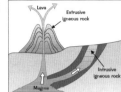
e) Intrusive: granite + gabbro.
Extrusive: basalt.

5) Air and gasses trapped during volcanic eruption and lava flow.

Pages 59, 60

1) Vertical column.

3) ~ 100.

5) Same number of electrons in outer shell hence similar chemical properties, form similarly charged ions etc.

7) Mendeleyev.

9) Group II.

11) **a)** H, I;   **e)** C;   **h)** F;   **k)** G;
b) D;   **f)** A;   **i)** A, E;   **l)** A;
c) B;   **g)** C,D,G,H,I;   **j)** H, I, C;   **m)** I.
d) B;

13) **a)** metals.   **c)** reactive, oil.   **e)** more.   **g)** 1⁺ ions.
b) soft, low.   **d)** easily.   **f)** sodium.

15) The zig-zag line divides metals from non-metals.

17) Right hand side.

19) Hydrogen.

21) 2^+ ions.

23) Francium.

25) It tells us that an atom of sodium has 11 electrons, 11 protons and 12 neutrons (and from this electronic configurations can be worked for the atom).

Pages 61, 62

1) They have 8 electrons in the outer shell (except for helium).

3) They have a full outer shell of electrons, making them stable so they have no need to react.

5) Helium is inert. Hydrogen is very reactive, highly explosive.

7) **a)** Increase down the group.

b)

Noble Gas	Atomic Number	Density g/cm³	Melting Point °C	Boiling Point °C
Helium	2	0.00017	-272	-269
Neon	10	0.00084	-248	-246
Argon	18	0.0016	-189	-186
Krypton	36	0.0034	-157	-153
Xenon	54	0.006	-112	-107
Radon	86	0.01	-71	-62

c) Increase in atomic mass.

9) Gives out a bright light when a current is passed through it.

11) Argon is denser than air, helium is less dense so the balloon rises rather than falls.

13) Diagram to show Neon — 2,8. 2 electrons in inner shell, 8 in outer shell, 10 protons, 10 neutrons. Argon — 2,8,8. 2 electrons in inner shell, 8 electrons in each of the 2 outer shells, 18 protons, 22 neutrons.

15) **a) & b)** 2 electrons
4 neutrons
3 protons

2 electrons,
2 neutrons,
2 protons

c) Lithium still has 3 protons in the nucleus. Helium has only two. Also lithium has two more neutrons.

17) **a)** Neon **b)** Neon **c)** Argon.

Pages 63, 64

1) **a)** They form an alkaline solution in water.

b) They all have one electron in the outer shell.

3) **a)** Purple. **b)** >>7.

5) Oxidation has occurred forming white sodium oxide.

7) **a)**

b) Lose an electron.
c) +1
d) Li⁺, K⁺

e) Potassium — It is easier for the outer electron of potassium to be lost as potassium atoms are bigger and the outer electron is further away from the nucleus, so is less firmly held. The alkali metals lose this electron in reactions.

9) A → 3, B → 1, C → 2.

11) K⁺, OH⁻.

13) Lithium - tarnishes slowly to give oxide layer; Sodium - tarnishes quickly to give oxide layer; Potassium - tarnishes very quickly to give oxide layer.

Pages 65, 66

1) They all have 7 electrons in the outer shell.

3) **a)** Below –101°C.

b) between –101°C and –35°C .

c) above –35°C.

5) **a)**

b) i) protons = 9 **ii)** neutrons = 10 **iii)** electrons = 9
iv) Electronic configuration is 2,7.

7) **a)**

b) Covalent.

9) **a)**
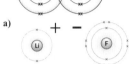
b)

11)

Halogen	Symbol	No. of Protons	No. of Neutrons	No. of Electrons	Mass Number	Atomic Number
Fluorine	F	9	10	9	19	9
Chlorine	Cl	17	18	17	35	17
Bromine	Br	35	45	35	80	35
Iodine	I	53	74	53	127	53
Astatine	At	85	125	85	210	85

13) Sublimation.

15) **a)** It is a solid that forms in a reaction, which either falls to the bottom or remains in suspension.

b) ⁻ or (s).

c) AgCl — white, AgBr — cream, AgI — yellow.

d) i) Sodium bromide + Silver nitrate → Sodium nitrate + Silver bromide.
ii) Sodium iodide + Silver nitrate → Silver iodide + Sodium nitrate.

17) Make a solution and mix with a solution of silver nitrate. Look at the colour of the precipitate formed.

Pages 67, 68

1) Ductile, high melting and boiling point, conduct heat and electricity, strong, shiny, and colourful compounds.

3) In the middle, between group II and group III.

5) 1 → B, 2 → D, 3 → C, 4 → A/E, 5 → A/E.

7)

Compound	Formula	Charge on Ion
a) Iron(II) oxide	FeO	Fe²⁺
b) Iron(III) chloride	FeCl₃	Fe³⁺
c) Iron(III) bromide	FeBr₃	Fe³⁺
d) Copper(II) oxide	CuO	Cu²⁺
e) Copper(I) chloride	CuCl	Cu⁺
f) Copper(II) chloride	CuCl₂	Cu²⁺
g) Iron(III) iodide	FeI₃	Fe³⁺

9) **a) i)** Fencing/gates. **ii)** Galvanising iron. **iii)** Wiring / pipes.

b) Others will be corroded by the water.

11) **a)**

Conductivity		Density	Malleability	Melting pt
Heat	Electricity			
Good	Good	Very dense	High	High

b) i) YCl. **ii)** YO. **iii)** Y₂O.

13) **a)** Water.

b) Heat them up.

c) Anhydrous.

d) Test for water

Page 69

1) **a)** High temperature uses such as cooking, engine components etc.

b) Mercury (liquid at room temperature); thermometers (liquid mercury expands on heating); some types of electrical switches.

3) **a)** Add weights to a length of the metal wire until it breaks. Repeat with wires of different materials but the same dimensions. The wire with the greatest tensile strength will support the most weight. You would have to protect yourself from the falling weights and snapping wire (wear safety shoes and glasses).

b) Test wires of equal length and cross-sectional area; place weights in similar way and conduct experiments at a similar temperature; make sure that the wire is undamaged i.e. no nicks or cuts.

5) **a)** Lead : dense, shields (stops) radiation; Aluminium : Low density, light and strong; Gold : does not corrode, shiny. (Uses as Q.13 or any other suitable answers)

b) Alloy. **c)** To create a substance with the properties we want.

d) The constituent metals are melted separately, and mixed together in exact proportions and allowed to solidify or the ores can be reduced together to give less exact results.

e) The metals are not chemically bonded to each other in exact proportions.

7) Metallic oxides are basic (pH above 7), non-metallic oxides are acidic (pH below 7).

Pages 70, 71

1) **a)** and **b)**

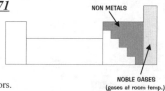

3) **a)** Insulators.

b) No free electrons. Covalent bonds between non-metal elements.

c) Carbon (in the form of graphite).

5) Non-metals: Some of them are gases at room temperature and pressure being diatomic molecules with only small forces between them (e.g. Chlorine). Also, they do not conduct electricity (as molecules) because the electrons in a covalent molecule are held tightly. The covalent bonds also mean that there boiling and melting points are relatively low.

Metals: Most have very high melting and boiling points owing to strong metallic bonds. Also, they are malleable and ductile because the giant structure can be distorted with the layers just sliding over one another.

7) A covalent bond.

9) **a)**

11) In general, non-metals tend to have diatomic or smaller molecules, not giant structures.

13) **a)** Acids.

b) In the sky they mix with the rain clouds forming acid, which then falls to ground causing losts of problems. This phenomenon is know as acid rain.

Pages 72, 73

1) F, F, T, T, T, T, T, F, T, F, F, T, T.

3) Neutral.

5) **a)** acid.   **c)** alkali.   **e)** acid.

b) alkali.   **d)** acid.

7) They can indicate the presence of an acid or an alkali, and the strength.

9)

Indicator	Colour in solution of:	
	Acid	Alkali
Universal Indicator	red to yellow	blue to violet
Red Litmus	no change	blue
Blue Litmus	red	no change
Phenolphthalein	colourless	purple
Methyl Orange	red	yellow
Methyl Red	red	yellow

11) **i)** 3. **ii)** 7. **iii)** 9. **iv)** 11-14. **v)** 14. **vi)** 1.

13) Add universal indicator to it and compare the colour produced with a colour chart / pH chart.

15) 1 = sulphuric acid — pH 2, 2 = vinegar – pH 4, 3 = water — pH 7, 4 = oven cleaner — pH 12.

Pages 74, 75

1) Water, hydrogen, carbon dioxide, salt.

3) Something which will react with acid to give a salt and water only (e.g. a metal oxide or metal hydroxide.)

5) Sulphuric acid - sulphates, hydrochloric acid - chlorides, nitric acid - nitrates.

7) **a)** The reaction between an acid and something else to bring the pH to 7.

b) The common crops like neutral or alkaline soil conditions.

c) lime.

9) **a)** Carbon Dioxide.

b) sodium hydrogencarbonate + sulphuric acid → sodium sulphate + carbon dioxide + water.

11) H^+ from acid and OH^- from alkali.

13) The reaction will give off H_2 which can be dangerous as it is a flammable gas and the reaction is vigorous.

Pages 76, 77

1) **a)** Metals put in order of reactivity (beginning with the most reactive).

b) Erosion of the material surface by chemical action.

c) Most violent reaction or fastest reaction.

d) K, Na, Al, Zn, Fe, Pb, Cu, Ag, Au.

e) 1 → C, 2 → A, 3 → D, 4 → B.

3) **a)** very high

b) Rubidium, Caesium.

c) X between K and Mg, Y between Fe and Au.

5) **a)** Something which removes oxygen or causes gain of electrons.

b) Above it.

c) Carbon is above iron in the reactivity series — the carbon in CO removes the oxygen from the iron.

d) Carbon monoxide + iron oxide → carbon dioxide + iron.

7) Its extraction is expensive as lots of electricity is needed for electrolysis of the ore and it cannot be extracted any other way because it is too reactive.

9) **a)** Sodium, potassium, magnesium, calcium.

b) Gold, silver, copper.

c) e.g. sodium oxide.

Page 78

1) Put on the roads to stop them icing over.

3) Brine

5) Decomposition of a salt using electricity.

7) A — sodium hydroxide,   D — Na^+ (sodium) ions,
B — Hydrogen gas,   E — OH^- (hydroxide) ions,
C — Chlorine gas,   F — Diaphragm.

9)

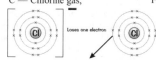

Page 79

1) $Cl_{2\,(g)} + 2NaOH_{(aq)} \rightarrow NaOCl_{(aq)} + NaCl_{(aq)} + H_2O_{(l)}$.

3) **a)** A = inverted funnel, B= delivery tube, C = trough.

b) H^+ ions in solution.

5) **a)** Oxidation is the loss of electrons. Since they both need one more electron to complete their outer electron shell, they remove electrons from other things and so oxidise them.

b) Chlorine is the stronger oxidising agent because it's smaller atomic radius means that it has greater effective charge, which makes it easier for it to remove electrons from other atoms.

c) i) $Cl_2 + 2e^- \rightarrow 2Cl^-$;
ii) $Br_2 + 2e^- \rightarrow 2Br^-$.

7) **a)** No.

b) Antiseptic.

Pages 80, 81

1) Match, egg, digestion, concrete, rust

3) Catalysts are used up in reactions - false; catalysts are specific to certain reactions - true; enzymes are biological catalysts - true; reactions slow if catalysts are used - false; enzymes increase the activation energy - false; reactions will speed up if they are heated - true; reactions slow down if they are diluted - true; increasing concentration increases the rate of reaction - true; pressure increases the rate of gaseous reaction - true; reactions are fast at the start - true.

5) Reacting magnesium with sulphuric acid, using a gas syringe to measure the amount of hydrogen given off etc.

7) **a), b)**

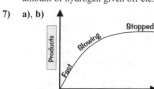

c) Reaction: start, middle, end
Speed: fast, slowing, stopped

Pages 82, 83

1) Collide; energy; collision theory; concentration; catalyst; faster; more often; energy; faster; particles; faster; surface area; faster; moderate; successful; collision; faster.

 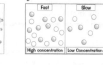

3) **c)** Reacting particles must collide with enough energy in order to react. (There is an activation energy barrier.)

5) **a) i)** B   **ii)** C
iii) A   **iv)** D

b) i) More particles due to increased concentration, so more chance of an effective collision and so a faster reaction.

ii) Same rate as the amount of particles in a certain volume is the same, so the collision rate will be the same. However there is more acid so assuming there are sufficient marble chips there will be a greater volume of gas produced.

iii) A larger surface area due to the smaller particles means there are more particles available for a collision and so available to react.

iv) Acid is colder so particles will have less kinetic energy giving a lower average speed of particles. This means that there will be a smaller number of collisions and of that number a smaller proportion will be able to provide the energy needed to surmount the activation energy barrier.

Pages 84, 85

1) a)

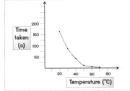

b) The higher the temperature, the less time is taken.

c)

Temperature (°C)	20	30	40	50	60	70
Time taken (s)	163	87	43	23	11	5
Rate (1/t)	0.0061	0.0115	0.0233	0.0435	0.0910	0.2000

d)

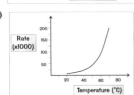

e) The higher the temperature, the faster the rate of reaction.

f) Higher temperatures give particles more energy, which makes them move faster. As the particles are moving faster, there are more collisions, and as they have more energy, more of these collisions are successful. Both mean a faster reaction rate.

3) a) $Mg_{(s)} + 2HCl_{(aq)} \rightarrow MgCl_{2\,(aq)} + H_{2\,(g)}$

b), c) and f) See graph

d) $22.5cm^3$

e) $40cm^3$ collected in 45s

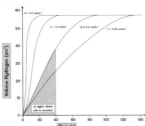

Page 86

1) a) Mass of marble, volume and concentration of acid, temperature.

b)

Time (s)	Mass (g)	Mass Lost (g)
0	100	0
30	99.8	0.2
60	99.6	0.4
90	99.4	0.6
120	99.2	0.8
150	99.0	1.0
180	98.8	1.2
210	98.6	1.4
240	98.45	1.55
270	98.30	1.7
300	98.20	1.8
330	98.15	1.85
360	98.15	1.85

Time (s)	Mass (g)	Mass Lost (g)
0	100	0
30	99.7	0.3
60	99.4	0.6
90	99.1	0.9
120	98.8	1.2
150	98.6	1.4
180	98.4	1.6
210	98.3	1.7
240	98.2	1.8
270	98.15	1.85
300	98.15	1.85
330	98.15	1.85
360	98.15	1.85

Time (s)	Mass (g)	Mass Lost (g)
0	100	0
30	99.0	1.0
60	98.5	1.5
90	98.3	1.7
120	98.2	1.8
150	98.15	1.85
180	98.15	1.85
210	98.15	1.85
240	98.15	1.85
270	98.15	1.85
300	98.15	1.85
330	98.15	1.85
360	98.15	1.85

c)

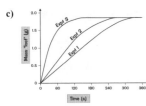

d) Experiment 3

e) The marble in Experiment 3 was powdered, and therefore had a greater surface area for other particles to collide with. This means there is more chance of collisions occurring, and therefore a faster rate of reaction.

f) Because the same mass of marble was used each time, and once all the marble had reacted, the experiment stopped.

g) Ex.1 — 0.4g/min; Ex.2 — 0.6g/min; Ex.3 — 1.5g/min

h) Because the reactants are being used up, and becoming less concentrated, so fewer collisions.

3) (anything reasonable) Slow reactions — rusting, decay, fading, rotting. Moderate reactions - digestion, paint drying, boiling an egg, jelly setting. Fast reactions - striking a match, burning, fireworks, explosives.

Pages 87, 88

1) a) Copper doesn't react **b)** Zinc reacts slowly **c)** Zinc and copper react much better together **d)** Copper acts as a catalyst. **e)** Copper is not used up, confirming its action as a catalyst.

3) a) Polluting gases - carbon monoxide, nitrogen oxides, unburnt petrol.

b) carbon dioxide, nitrogen, water vapour.

5) Catalysts speed up the reaction therefore it takes less time to make more product. Catalysts also lower the operating temperature and this saves money.

7) a) Optimum temperature is between 30 and 40 °C

b) Above this temperature the enzyme does not work as well as it becomes denatured.

Pages 89, 90

1) a) amylase, maltase and sucrase

b) Enzymes are specific to one type of reaction / not all enzymes work on all substrates / Trypsin is an enzyme designed to digest protein, not starch.

3) a) Food spoilage is caused by reactions of bacteria and fungi.

b) The temperature in the fridge is about 5 °C and this slows the bacteria's reactions.

c) Freezing reduces the temperature further and effectively stops the spoilage reactions. Microbes can not grow when the available water in the food is frozen.

5) a) $C_6H_{12}O_6 \rightarrow 2\ C_2H_5OH + 2CO_2 + energy$

b)

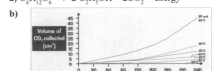

c) Optimum temperature is between 35 and 40 °C

d)

Temperature (°C)	20	25	30	35	40	45	50	55
Rate (cm³/min)	2	4	8	20	20	4	2	0

e)

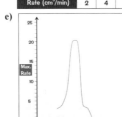

f) Optimum temperature = 35 °C - see graph

g) Above the optimum temperature the enzyme is denatured

h) Fermentation products - beer, lager, wine, bread

Pages 91, 92

1) a) $NH_3 + HCl \rightarrow NH_4Cl$ $NH_4Cl \rightarrow NH_3 + HCl$

b) reversible reaction - the reaction goes both ways, reactants make products but products also break down to reactants.

c) $NH_3 + HCl \rightleftharpoons NH_4Cl$

3) a) 1 = balanced 2 = equilibrium 3 = equilibrium 4 = static 5 = down 6 = up 7 = activity 8 = change 9 = dynamic 10 = dynamic 11 = closed 12 = open

b) dynamic

c) closed

d) open system. The equilibrium would cease to be an equilibrium.

5) a) Increasing temperature will favour the products (reaction goes to right).

b) Increasing pressure will move equilibrium to left (to decrease volume, as fewer moles of gas on left).

c) Doubling the concentration of N_2O_4 will favour the products (send the reaction to the right).

7) a) $N_{2(g)} + 3H_{2(g)} \rightleftharpoons 2NH_{3(g)}$

b) Iron catalyst

c) Catalyst speeds up reaction.

d) Fine pellets have a large surface area - more contact area for reactants.

e) Optimum conditions from graph are high pressure and low temperature.

f) High pressure sends the reaction to the right and favours more product (4 moles of gas on left : only 2 on right).

g) Extreme high pressure is expensive and dangerous. 200 atms represents a working compromise. Lower temperatures give a higher percentage yield but take much longer to do so. 450 °C gives an acceptable yield very quickly (balance between % yield and RATE of reaction).

Pages 93, 94

1) energy (heat), exothermic, energy (heat), endothermic, Exothermic, hot, given out, Endothermic, cold, taken in, DH, endothermic, negative, energy, exothermic, endothermic, energy, break, energy, made.

3) a) Breaking one N-N bond needs 945kJ/mol

b) Breaking the H-H bond needs 435kJ/mol

c) Making the N-H bond releases 389kJ/mol

d)

$$N{\equiv}N + 3{\times}(H{-}H) \rightleftharpoons 2{\times}\left(\begin{array}{c} H \\ N \\ H\quad H \end{array}\right)$$

e) Breaking reactant bonds needs
N = N + (3 x H-H) =
945 + (3 x 435) = 2250kJ/mol

f) Making product releases 6 x N-H = 6x389 = 2334kJ/mol

g) Overall energy change is 2250 - 2334 = -84kJ/mol
More energy is released. It is exothermic, overall energy change is -84kJ/mol

5) a) 4 x C-H (413) = 1652kJ/mol
2 x 0=0 (497) = 994kJ/mol
Total = 2646kJ/mol

b) 2 x C=0 (740) = 1480kJ/mol
4 x O-H (463) = 1852kJ/mol
Total = 3332kJ/mol

c) Overall energy change
= energy in - energy out
= 2646 - 3332
= -686kJ/mol (exothermic)

d)

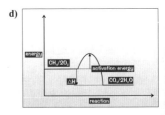

e) exothermic